Birds

Examining Your Environment

John C. MacBean
Adam Stecher
Daniel F. Wentworth
J. Kenneth Couchman

Mine Publications, Incorporated
25 Groveland Terrace, Minneapolis, Minn. 55403

John C. MacBean
Science Consultant
Niagara South Board of Education
Port Colborne, Ontario

Adam Stecher
Assistant Superintendent
Perth County Board of Education
Stratford, Ontario

Daniel F. Wentworth
Science Consultant
Hamilton Board of Education
Hamilton, Ontario

J. Kenneth Couchman
Co-ordinator of Programs, Junior Division
Hamilton-Wentworth Roman Catholic Separate School Board
Hamilton, Ontario

ISBN 0-03-922172-5

Distributed in the United States of America by
Mine Publications, Inc.,
25 Groveland Terrace,
Minneapolis, Minnesota 55403.

Published simultaneously in Great Britain by
Blond Educational Ltd.,
Iliffe House, Oadby, Leicestershire, England.

Printed in Canada 2 3 4 5 75 74 73 72 71

Contents

Introduction

This book is divided into four chapters, Live Birds, Birds' Eggs, Birds' Nests and Dead Birds. The activities in each section are specifically designed to get you involved with birds in their natural environment instead of birds in books. The chapters and the activities are separate and individual. You can do those that interest you without feeling that all the activities must be done in sequence. Some of the activities could best be done during certain seasons of the year, such as collecting birds' nests in the autumn, or studying birds' eggs in the spring.

The book deals mainly with how to look at birds. The authors have attempted to develop certain skills. If these skills are mastered by you and applied to birds, a tremendous amount of general knowledge regarding our feathered friends can be collected. It is not only hoped that you will learn a great deal about birds but that you will also have a better understanding and appreciation of them.

One thing this book does not attempt to do is to develop skills in bird identification. There are too many other excellent books written specifically about that subject. Instead, this book will give you a new and exciting way to observe birds.

Examining Your Environment
Other and Forthcoming Titles

Mini-climates

Pollution

Running Water

Snow and Ice

Trees

Live Birds 1

1. Live Birds

This bird is man's helper. What kind of bird is it?

Since birds provide man with pleasure, beauty, often companionship and are in many instances helpful, more has been written about them than any other species of wild animal. Birds, like man, build homes, hunt for food, raise young and face many problems; therefore, the study of birds may make you more knowledgeable about yourself.

The following activities are designed to get you involved with birds. They are developed such that you will carry out first hand research with birds, and if carried out correctly, will give you a better understanding and appreciation of them.

Activity 1:

What enables birds and airplanes to fly?

We live at the bottom of an ocean of air. Air is a substance which has weight, therefore, it exerts a pressure. This pressure is exerted equally in all directions. If we look at the wing of a bird or airplane we see that it has a special structure.

The special structure of the wing causes the air pressure balance to be upset. The air particles which meet and pass over the wing must travel farther than those which pass under the wing. This results in a difference in *air pressure*. The pressure above is less than that below and the structure acquires *lift* (the ability to stay in the air) for as long as a steady stream of air continues to flow over the wing.

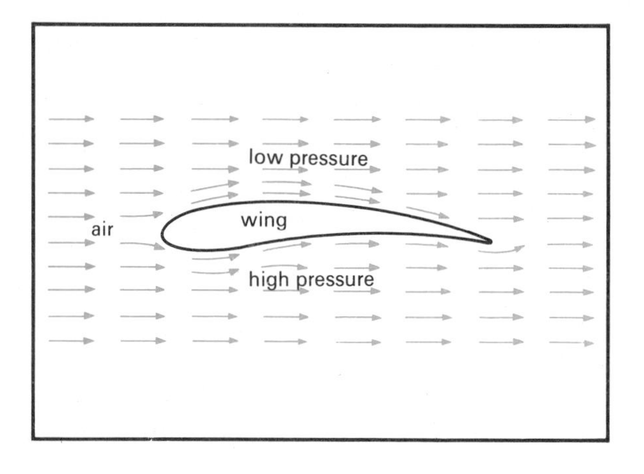

Cross section of an airplane wing.

What do you think will happen to the paper when you blow air over it?

What will happen when air is blown through the tentlike structure?

What will happen to the two cans when air is blown between them?

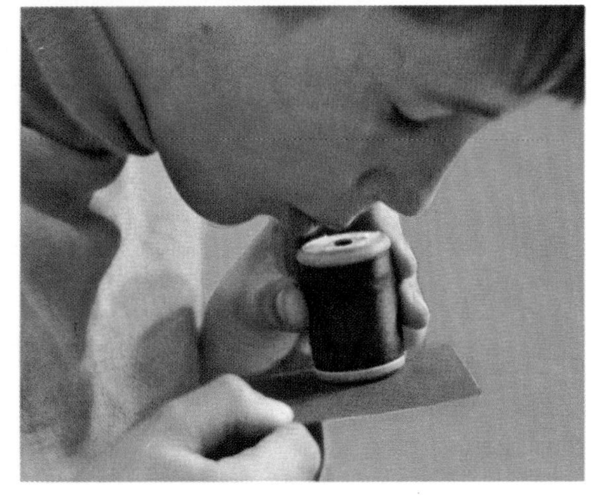

What will happen to the cardboard?

What will happen to the piece of paper?

Use the following materials and illustrations to experiment with air pressure. Assemble together two sheets of paper 8½ inches by 11 inches, two empty pop cans, ten straws, a large wooden spool (like the type which thread comes on), a piece of cardboard 3 inches by 3 inches, a piece of paper 6 inches by 2 inches, and a pencil at least 4 inches long.

Perform the five experiments as they are illustrated but try to predict the results before you actually conduct each.

Digging Deeper

How did the results of each experiment differ from what you had predicted?

Explain what happened in each experiment. Can you explain the result in terms of air pressure?

What keeps a bird in the air? Where does the lift take place? Why?

Are there other factors which contribute to a bird's ability to fly?

What do reference books contain regarding the theory of flight (aerodynamics)?

What keeps a kite up in the air?

Explain in terms of air pressure how this tern is able to fly.

Activity 2:

How can the fright distance *of a bird be measured?*

Birds are very timid creatures and, as such, sudden or quick movements will cause them to take flight. Since some birds tend to be more timid than others, each type of bird will have its own fright distance. A bird will allow you to get only so close and then fly away. This distance is the fright distance.

For this activity you will need a piece of white cloth (handkerchief size) for a marker, a tape measure (50 feet or 100 feet), a pencil, and a clipboard and paper to record your data.

Take your equipment and go for a walk around your school or home.

When you sight a bird, hold the white cloth in one of your hands and walk slowly towards it. Make a mental note of the exact location of the bird.

The moment that the bird flies away drop the cloth, and walk to the spot where the bird was.

Measure the distance from where you are standing to the cloth. This is the fright distance of the bird.

To be more accurate repeat this activity several times, if possible, with the same bird or with birds of the same species. Once you have obtained a number of measurements calculate the average fright distance of that species of bird.

Your fright distance data could be recorded on a chart.

Digging Deeper

What bird in your area allowed you to get closest to it?

What bird in your area had the largest fright distance?

Which birds in your area seem to be the least timid? most timid?

Which birds do you think would be most easily tamed via bird feeders, birdhouses, and birdbaths?

Order the birds in your table from least to most timid.

How would whistling or shouting change the fright distances of the birds which you tested?

Measuring the fright distance of birds.

Bird	Fright distance in feet								Average	Remarks
	1	2	3	4	5	6	7	Total		
Robin										
Sparrow										

Activity 3:

What are the flight patterns of the birds in your area?

If you conducted the preceding activity (fright distances) you probably noticed that different species had different flight patterns. A flight pattern is how a particular bird flies through the air.

For example, some birds fly like this—flap, flap, flap, flap—sail; flap, flap, flap, flap—sail; flap, flap, flap, flap—sail in a

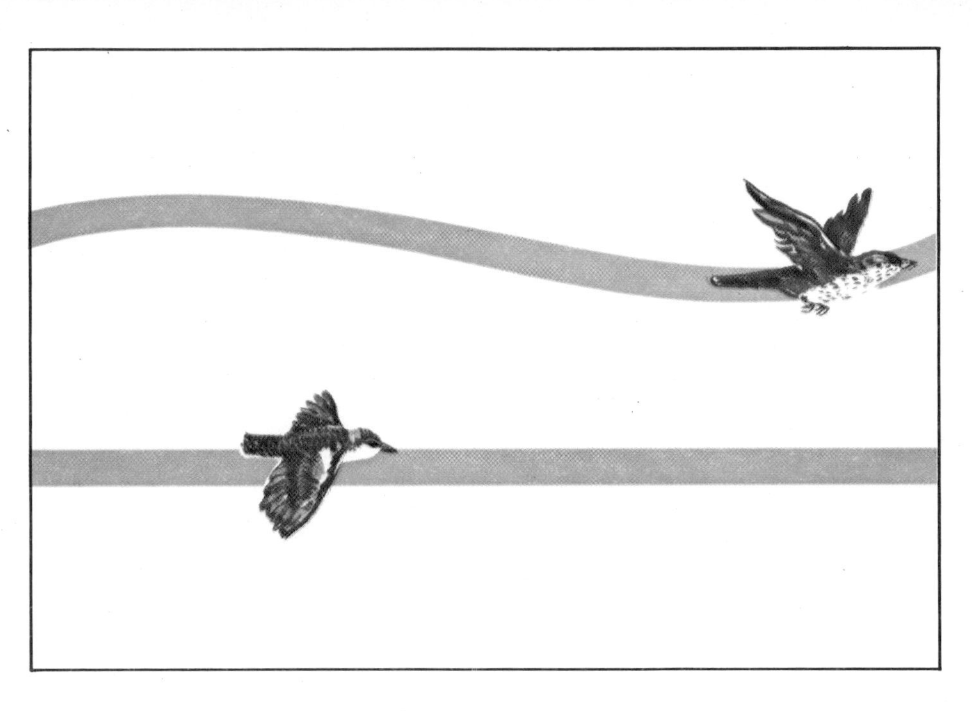

What is this student doing?

straight line; others go flap, flap, flap, flap, flap, flap, flap—in circles; while still others hover and glide, hover and glide, hover and glide—in up and down patterns. Try to sketch the flight patterns of the different birds in your locality.

Gather a clipboard, a pencil, some paper, and if possible, a book which would aid you in identifying some of the birds you will see. (*A Field Guide to the Birds* by Roger T. Peterson is excellent.)

Find an open spot around the school, by a lake or pond, or near a woodlot, and make yourself comfortable since this type of activity requires patience and stillness.

When you sight a bird, observe its flight pattern as it flies by you.

Record your observations while you are still watching the bird or immediately after it has flown out of sight. A good way to record the flight pattern is simply by drawing a line. The examples will provide guidance for the type of line drawings you could make.

Write the name or sketch a picture of the bird beside each flight pattern and put your name and the date on the recording sheet. Later when you return to your classroom or home, all the data you collected could be displayed in a mural.

Digging Deeper

What bird in your area has the most graceful flight pattern?

Does wing shape, such as long-narrow or short-broad, determine or affect a bird's flight pattern?

Does the beat of the wings, such as strong beat or fluttery beat, affect the bird's flight pattern?

Does each species of bird have its own flight pattern?

Branching Out

Consider this list of descriptive words: jerky, bouncy, darting, circling, straight, bounding, erratic, twinkling, irregular, swooping, unsteady, soaring, zigzagging. Select and record the words which best describe the types of flight patterns you recorded.

A good mural should have a title, flow of colour, balance, and a minimum number of colours.

Bouncy flight pattern.

Study the following list of words: rapid, strong, steady, deep (wings almost touch under body), shallow, fluttery, fast, slow, weak, regular, hovering, easy, mechanical, wavering. Observe the wing beat of birds while they are flying. Use a word or combination of these words to describe the wing beat of different birds, i.e., swan—steady deep beats.

What word would describe this wing beat?

Make line drawings to illustrate some of the wing beats and speeds of birds.

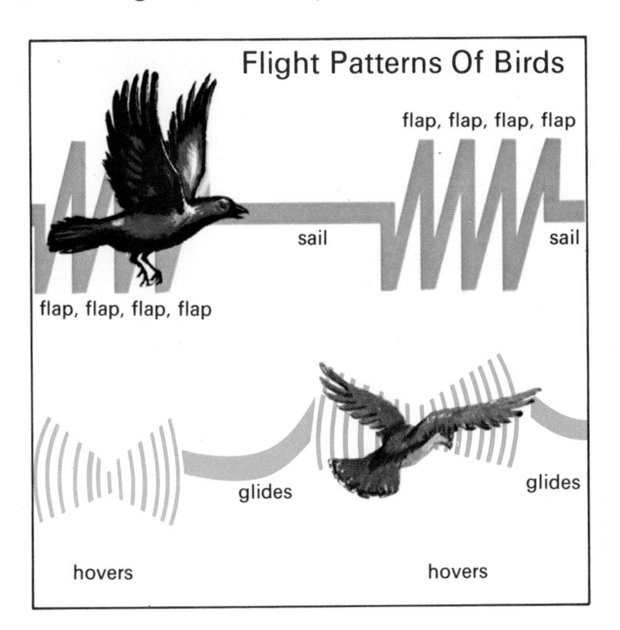

Which of the following sketches show the position of the wings in relation to the body when the bird is gliding or sailing?

How are the tips of the wings held? Are they curved upward, curved downward, or straight out?

Obtain a stopwatch and attempt to time the speed of different birds. (Velocity or speed, equals distance divided by time.) List the factors you will have to consider when doing this activity.

Consult an encyclopedia to help you make a list of birds which cannot fly. Beside each, state the reason(s) why the bird can't fly.

Activity 4:

What is in a box of bird seed?

In order to maintain their strength and provide the fabulous amounts of energy which flying requires, birds must continually search for food, such as seeds, insects, or other small animals. Man sometimes attempts to aid the birds by putting out such things as seeds, crumbs, animal fats and other scraps. Let's take a closer look at what a box of commercially prepared bird seed contains. You may be surprised at what you find.

Study the contents of a box of commercial bird seed.

Show the different kinds of seeds that you found, and the number of each on a graph.

These children are discovering what a box of bird seed contains.

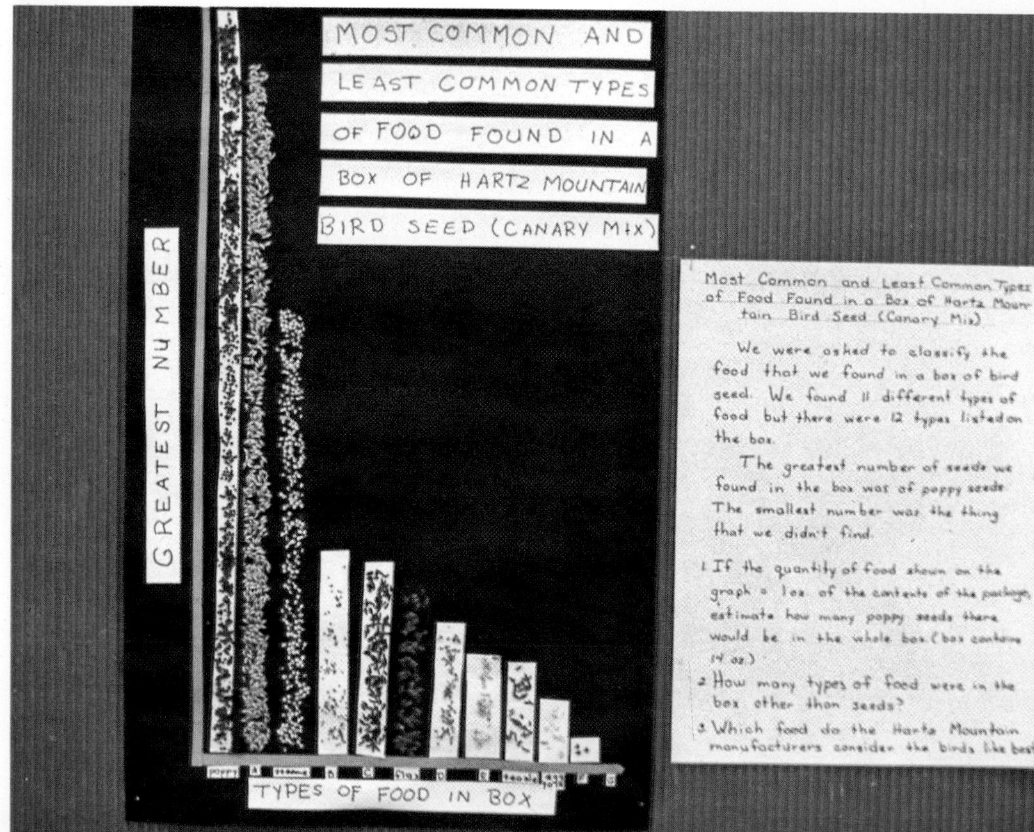

Prepare three questions about the data on your graph and see if your friends can answer them.

Digging Deeper

Did you discover some things that were not seeds in your sample? How many were there?

How many different kinds of seeds and other things were there in the box? Try to identify all of them.

In a box of bird seed there is always one type of seed which is more common than another. What is the most common type of seed in the box? the least common type of seed?

Are all the seeds approximately the same size?

How many individual particles do you estimate to be in the box?

Why is there a variety of seeds in the box?

What is meant by the expression *net weight* on the box?

If you planted these seeds would they grow?

Branching Out

Classify the birds in your locality under the following headings: seed eaters, insect eaters, meat eaters.

Examine pictures of birds' bills. How are the bills of seed eaters suited for the job of cracking the seeds?

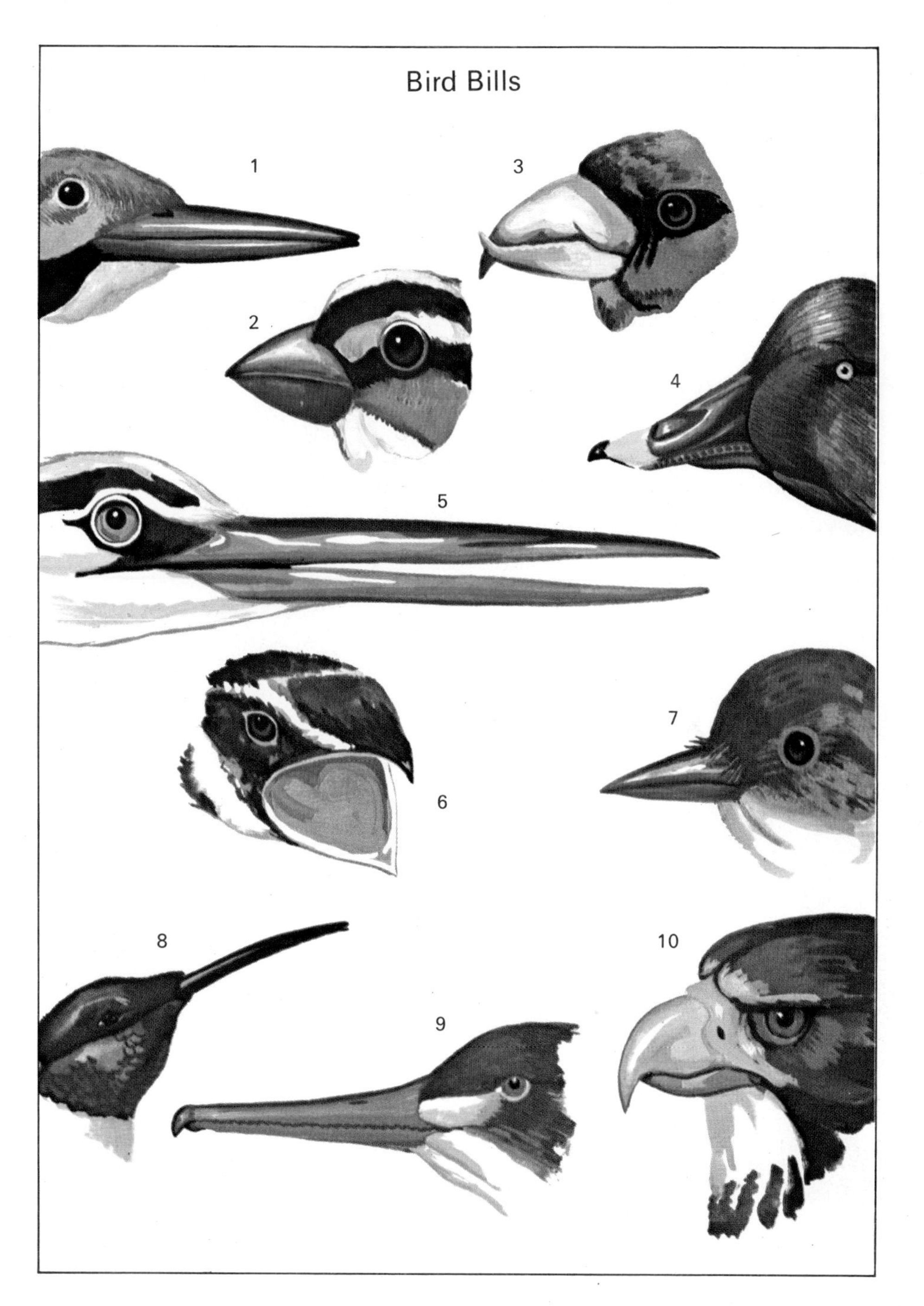

1. The chisel-tipped bill of the woodpecker is used to dig holes in wood.
2. The stout bill of the sparrow is used to crack hard seeds.
3. The twisted bill of the crossbill serves to extract seeds from cones of evergreens.
4. The strainerlike bill of the duck is used to sieve food from the water.
5. The spearlike bill of the heron is used to catch fish and frogs.
6. The wide-gaped bill of the nighthawk is used to capture insects on the wing in full flight.
7. The straight bill of the phoebe is used to capture insects.
8. The long thin bill of the hummingbird reaches deep into the throats of flowers.
9. The saw-edged bill of the merganser or shell-drake is used to catch fish.
10. The hooked bill of the hawk is used to tear its prey of mice.

Make a list of plants in your area that furnish food for birds in the winter. To compile your list look in fields, along roadsides, and in gardens. What plants have bird tracks around them in the winter? Which shrubs, vines and trees have fruits that stay on them for most of the year? Use the illustrations as a guide.

1. Flowering dogwood
2. Poison ivy
3. Staghorn sumac
4. Wild rose
5. Panicled dogwood
6. Woodbine
7. Apple
8. Wild grape
9. Arrow wood
10. Red cedar
11. Wild raisin
12. Thorn apple

Plants That Furnish Food For Birds

Which birds eat in groups? Which eat singly?

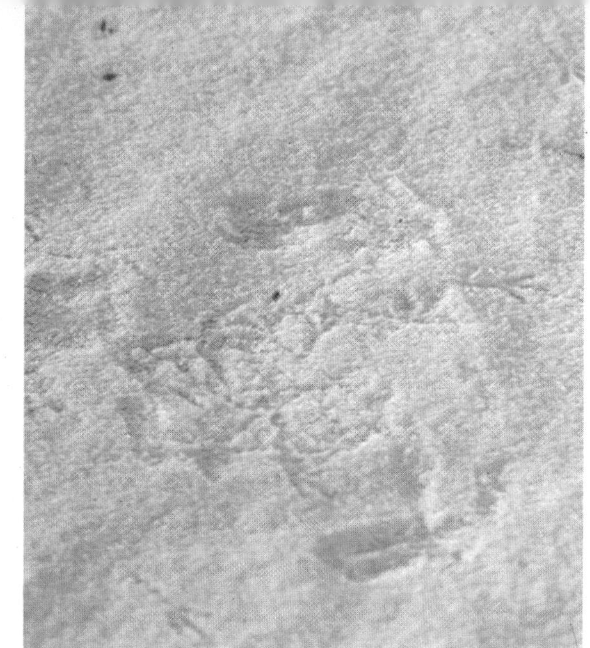

Do the birds that made these tracks eat in groups or by themselves?

Slate junco at a platform feeder.

Activity 5:

What type of bird feeders can be built for birds?

There is a tremendous variety of types of bird feeders. Some of the more simple types of feeders could be established very easily and quickly, while the more elaborate types would require much time and skill to put into operation. Examine the following diagrams of bird feeders. Construct one or two that would complement your handyman ability, materials available, and degree of interest.

Window sill feeder.

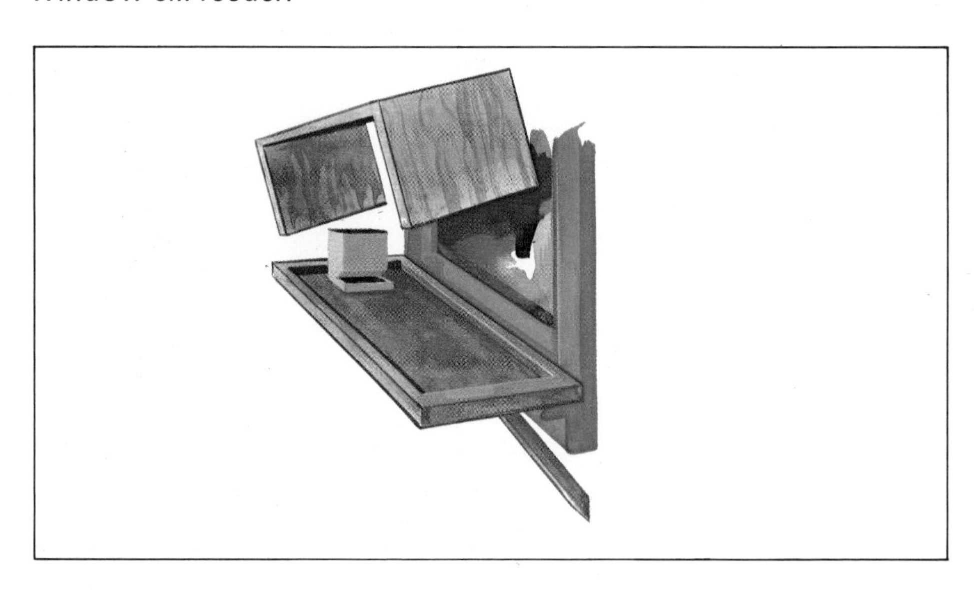

Simple platform feeder on a pole.

saw

brace

suet
placed in holes

end of tree trunk (Christmas tree)

Suet log.

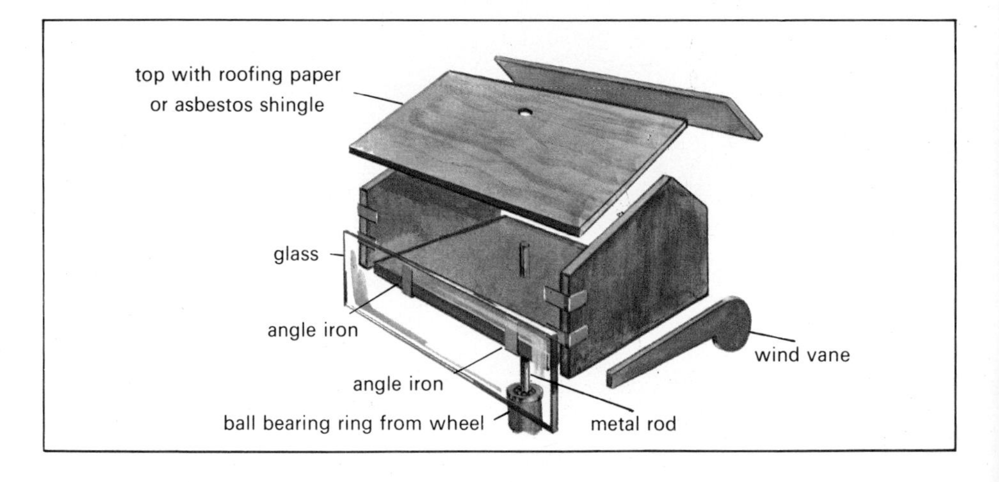

Rotating glass-backed all-weather bird feeder.

Pine cone with melted suet or peanut butter.

Woven string bag feeder with suet.

Trolley feeder on pulleys.

Peanut butter board.

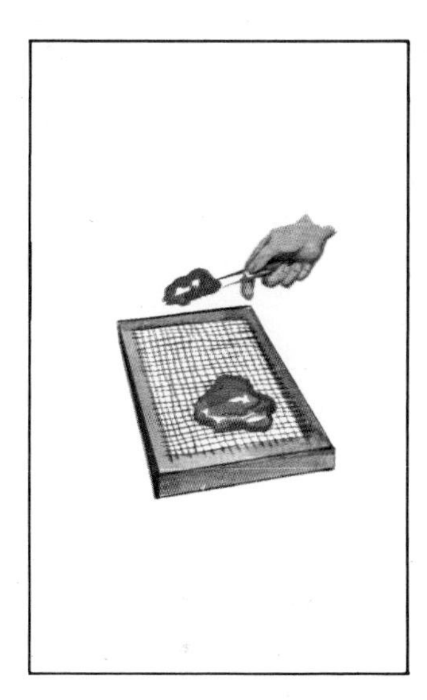

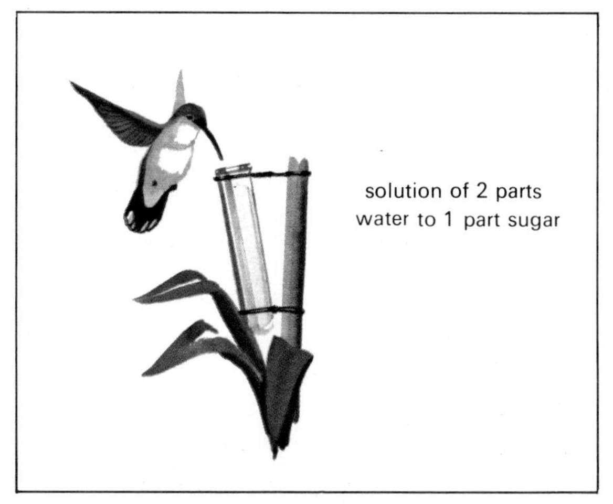

Test tube feeder for hummingbirds.

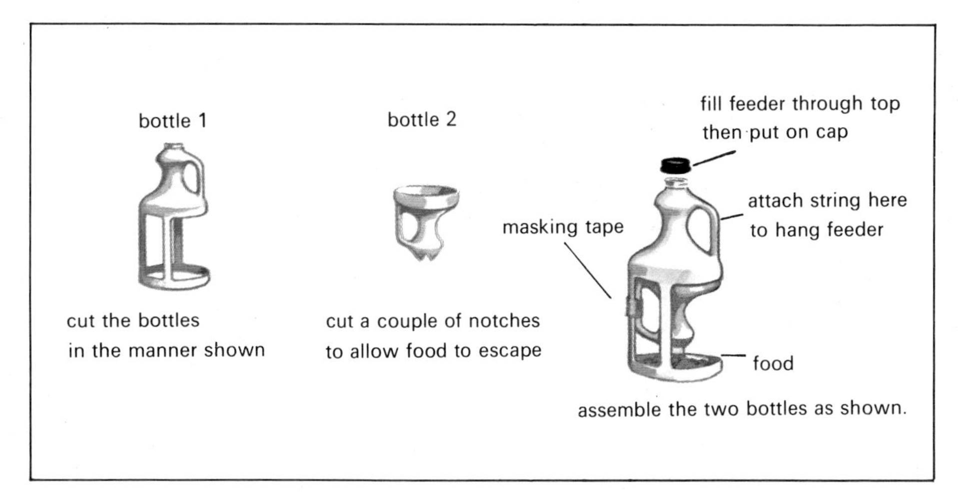

Bleach bottle feeder.

If you set up feeders, give careful consideration to the following items:

(a) When is the best time of year to establish a feeding station?
(b) How will it be protected from the enemies of birds, i.e., cats, squirrels?
(c) What is the best location for the feeder with respect to trees, buildings, open spaces?
(d) What type of food will be used, i.e., crumbs, peanut butter, raisins, variety of seeds?
(e) Birds need water to drink and dust to have a dust bath. How will these be provided?
(f) If you go away on vacation who will maintain the feeding station? Birds become *very* dependent on sources of food, especially in the winter.

Name ______ Bird Feeder Data Sheet Date ______

Bird	Time	Frequency of visits	Weather– temperature precipitation wind	Number of birds	Ate alone or in company	Ate at tray– carried food away	Fought over food	Food eaten	Drank water

Bird feeders provide an excellent opportunity for you to observe birds. Keep a pair of binoculars handy to help you observe the habits of the visitors to your feeding station. A good bird book should be available to aid in identifying the birds. Your observations could be recorded daily in a chart like the one shown.

Digging Deeper

Which birds prefer to eat on the ground?

If you have more than one type of feeder, which attracts the most birds? What factors might account for this?

Which birds eat only suet? only seeds?

Does weather influence the type of bird that visits your feeding station?

Which birds usually eat without fighting?

Do certain birds prefer a certain time of day to visit your station?

What is the frequency of birds taking a dust bath? Which birds take dust baths most often?

How long does a particular bird remain at the feeding station during any one visit?

Which birds are bullies?

Branching Out

Set up a bird watching station at a classroom or home window. This could be done by designing a boothlike compartment from a large cardboard box. The station should include binoculars, clock, recording materials, a bird identification book, and a camera, if possible.

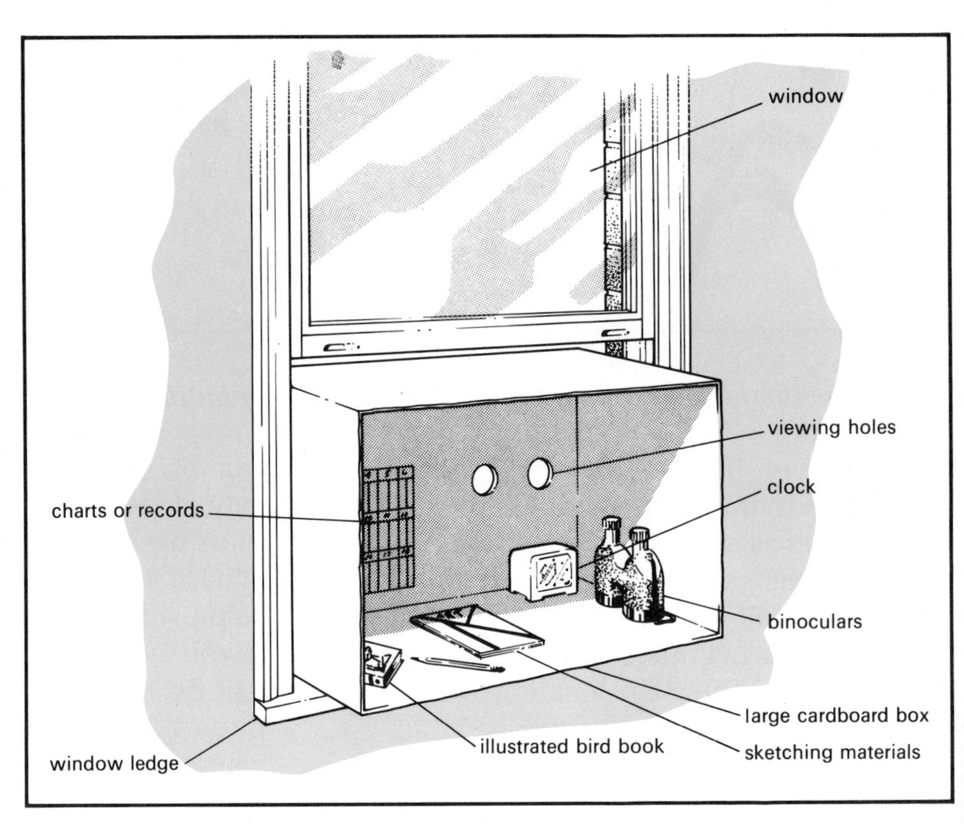

A bird watching station.

Observe how the birds move, land, peck, drink, perch, and fly away. If you are going to use a field guide for birds, have your teacher or a local bird watcher explain the proper use of the book, since it is set up in a very special way.

Activity 6:

How can birds be identified?

There have been so many excellent books written on how to identify birds that this activity will only attempt to steer you toward the long, hard road of bird identification. Bird identification requires much skill, practice, time, interest and patience. If you begin with some of these fundamental ground rules, it could develop into a most interesting and rewarding pastime.

Learn the basic terminology pertaining to a bird's anatomy. It is very important to have a frame of reference about the bird's physical features, especially in relation to its field-marks. That is, if you see a bird flying away from you and it displays an orange rump, you could probably be certain it is a killdeer.

Never be in a hurry to label a bird. Consider as many factors as you can before your final decision is made. A field guide will provide many more specific terms regarding field-marks of birds.

Set up some of your own basic guidelines or yardsticks for identification. The following may be helpful:

size	larger than or smaller than a sparrow, or a crow, or an owl
shape	chunky, slender, owl-shaped
sight and action	forked tail, spotted breast, crest on crown, red legs, hooked bill, wing bars, rounded short wings and long tail, hops, walks, runs up and down a tree trunk
sound	kil-deer, kil-deer, gah-gah
site	paddles by water, sits motionless in tall trees, on lawns, in open fields and pastures, around barns.

Learn some of the different bird families—Plovers, Owls, and Hawks.

Learn how to use a field guide book, such as *A Field Guide to the Birds* by R. T. Peterson, or *How to Know the Birds* by R. T. Peterson.

Digging Deeper

How many different bird families are there?

How is a field guide book set up so that birds can be identified?

How many terms are used in a book on birds to describe parts of a bird's anatomy?

Use a field guide book to discover what a bird's field-marks are.

Branching Out

What do these symbols indicate?

♀ ♂

What is meant by palmate, semipalmate?

Make sketches of the different feet and bills of birds you see.

Classify these birds according to their type of bill or foot.

Obtain records of bird songs and calls. Most birds' songs are sung at a pitch higher than the highest note on a piano. Some birds actually sing in chords (more than one note at a time). Play the records at a slower speed and you should be able to detect some of these subtleties.

Do a detailed study of one bird. The study could be pursued under headings such as: Identification and Classification, Nesting, Habitat, Food, Diseases, Enemies, Migration, Range.

Science museums usually have a *field check-list* for birds. Write to your nearest science museum to obtain a check-list and instructions regarding its use.

Activity 7:

How can a plaster cast of a bird's footprints be made?

Obtain the following materials: strips of cardboard 1 inch by 8 inches, plaster of Paris, coffee stir stick, 2 paper clips, salt, borax, water, old toothbrush, paper cups, paint, a paint brush, and shellac.

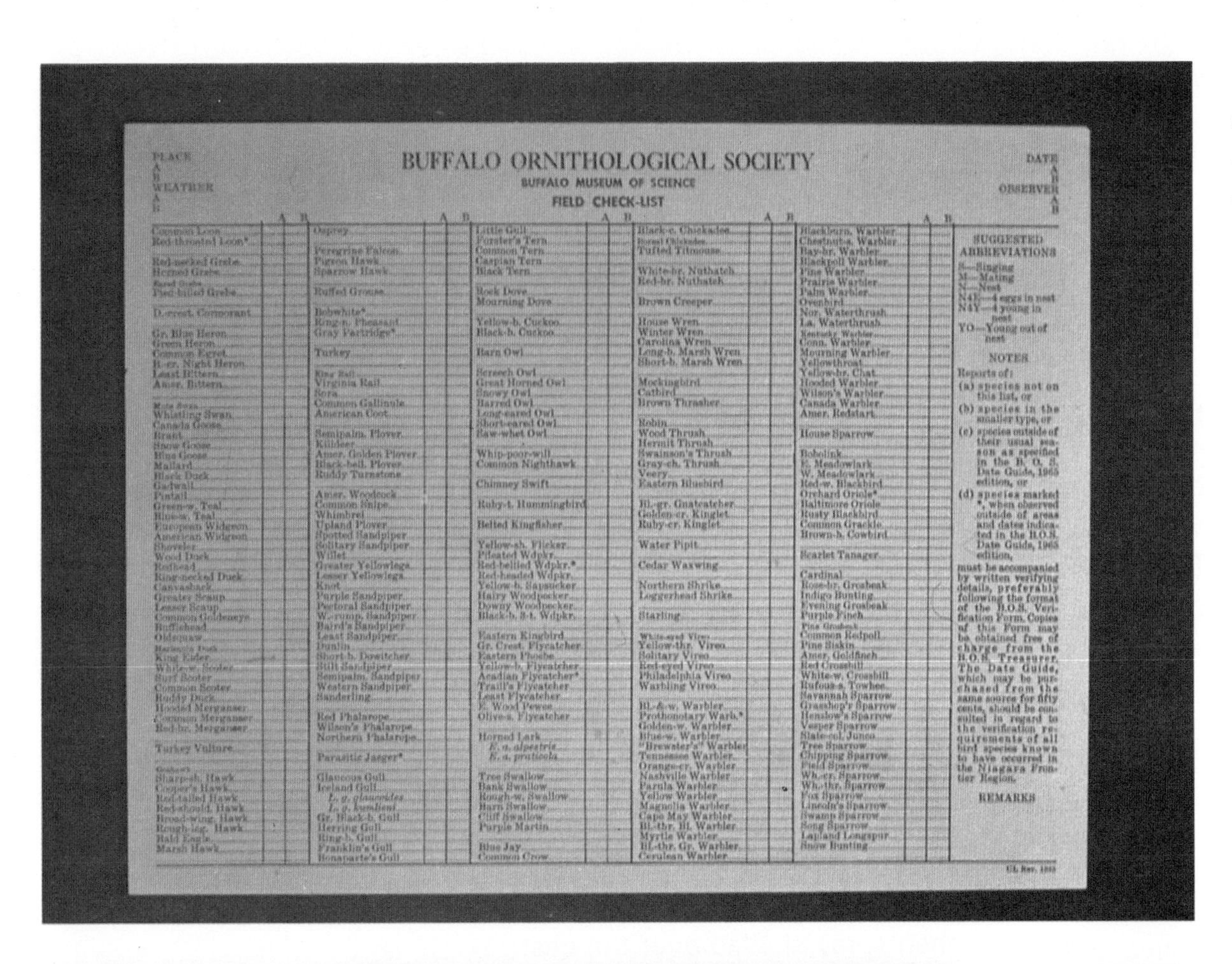

PLACE
A
B
WEATHER
A
B

BUFFALO ORNITHOLOGICAL SOCIETY
BUFFALO MUSEUM OF SCIENCE
FIELD CHECK-LIST

DATE
A
B
OBSERVER
A
B

Common Loon
Red-throated Loon*
Red-necked Grebe
Horned Grebe
Eared Grebe
Pied-billed Grebe
D.-crest. Cormorant
Gr. Blue Heron
Green Heron
Common Egret
B.-cr. Night Heron
Least Bittern
Amer. Bittern
Mute Swan
Whistling Swan
Canada Goose
Brant
Snow Goose
Blue Goose
Mallard
Black Duck
Gadwall
Pintail
Green-w. Teal
Blue-w. Teal
European Widgeon
American Widgeon
Shoveler
Wood Duck
Redhead
Ring-necked Duck
Canvasback
Greater Scaup
Lesser Scaup
Common Goldeneye
Bufflehead
Oldsquaw
Harlequin Duck
King Eider
White-w. Scoter
Surf Scoter
Common Scoter
Ruddy Duck
Hooded Merganser
Common Merganser
Red-br. Merganser
Turkey Vulture
Goshawk
Sharp-sh. Hawk
Cooper's Hawk
Red-tailed Hawk
Red-should. Hawk
Broad-wing. Hawk
Rough-leg. Hawk
Bald Eagle
Marsh Hawk

Osprey
Peregrine Falcon
Pigeon Hawk
Sparrow Hawk
Ruffed Grouse
Bobwhite*
Ring-n. Pheasant
Gray Partridge*
Turkey
King Rail
Virginia Rail
Sora
Common Gallinule
American Coot
Semipalm. Plover
Killdeer
Amer. Golden Plover
Black-bell. Plover
Ruddy Turnstone
Amer. Woodcock
Common Snipe
Whimbrel
Upland Plover
Spotted Sandpiper
Solitary Sandpiper
Willet
Greater Yellowlegs
Lesser Yellowlegs
Knot
Purple Sandpiper
Pectoral Sandpiper
W.-rump. Sandpiper
Baird's Sandpiper
Least Sandpiper
Dunlin
Short-b. Dowitcher
Stilt Sandpiper
Semipalm. Sandpiper
Western Sandpiper
Sanderling
Red Phalarope
Wilson's Phalarope
Northern Phalarope
Parasitic Jaeger*
Glaucous Gull
Iceland Gull
L. g. glaucoides
L. g. kumlieni
Gr. Black-b. Gull
Herring Gull
Ring-b. Gull
Franklin's Gull
Bonaparte's Gull

Little Gull
Forster's Tern
Common Tern
Caspian Tern
Black Tern
Rock Dove
Mourning Dove
Yellow-b. Cuckoo
Black-b. Cuckoo
Barn Owl
Screech Owl
Great Horned Owl
Snowy Owl
Barred Owl
Long-eared Owl
Short-eared Owl
Saw-whet Owl
Whip-poor-will
Common Nighthawk
Chimney Swift
Ruby-t. Hummingbird
Belted Kingfisher
Yellow-sh. Flicker
Pileated Wdpkr.
Red-bellied Wdpkr.*
Red-headed Wdpkr.
Yellow-b. Sapsucker
Hairy Woodpecker
Downy Woodpecker
Black-b. 3-t. Wdpkr.
Eastern Kingbird
Gr. Crest. Flycatcher
Eastern Phoebe
Yellow-b. Flycatcher
Acadian Flycatcher*
Traill's Flycatcher
Least Flycatcher
E. Wood Pewee
Olive-s. Flycatcher
Horned Lark
E. a. alpestris
E. a. praticola
Tree Swallow
Bank Swallow
Rough-w. Swallow
Barn Swallow
Cliff Swallow
Purple Martin
Blue Jay
Common Crow

Black-c. Chickadee
Boreal Chickadee
Tufted Titmouse
White-br. Nuthatch
Red-br. Nuthatch
Brown Creeper
House Wren
Winter Wren
Carolina Wren
Long-b. Marsh Wren
Short-b. Marsh Wren
Mockingbird
Catbird
Brown Thrasher
Robin
Wood Thrush
Hermit Thrush
Swainson's Thrush
Gray-ch. Thrush
Veery
Eastern Bluebird
Bl.-gr. Gnatcatcher
Golden-cr. Kinglet
Ruby-cr. Kinglet
Water Pipit
Cedar Waxwing
Northern Shrike
Loggerhead Shrike
Starling
White-eyed Vireo
Yellow-thr. Vireo
Solitary Vireo
Red-eyed Vireo
Philadelphia Vireo
Warbling Vireo
Bl.-&-w. Warbler
Prothonotary Warb.*
Golden-w. Warbler
Blue-w. Warbler
"Brewster's" Warbler
Tennessee Warbler
Orange-cr. Warbler
Nashville Warbler
Parula Warbler
Yellow Warbler
Magnolia Warbler
Cape May Warbler
Bl.-thr. Bl. Warbler
Myrtle Warbler
Bl.-thr. Gr. Warbler
Cerulean Warbler

Blackburn. Warbler
Chestnut-s. Warbler
Bay-br. Warbler
Blackpoll Warbler
Pine Warbler
Prairie Warbler
Palm Warbler
Ovenbird
Nor. Waterthrush
La. Waterthrush
Kentucky Warbler
Conn. Warbler
Mourning Warbler
Yellowthroat
Yellow-br. Chat
Hooded Warbler
Wilson's Warbler
Canada Warbler
Amer. Redstart
House Sparrow
Bobolink
E. Meadowlark
W. Meadowlark
Red-w. Blackbird
Orchard Oriole*
Baltimore Oriole
Rusty Blackbird
Common Grackle
Brown-h. Cowbird
Scarlet Tanager
Cardinal
Rose-br. Grosbeak
Indigo Bunting
Evening Grosbeak
Purple Finch
Pine Grosbeak
Common Redpoll
Pine Siskin
Amer. Goldfinch
Red Crossbill
White-w. Crossbill
Rufous-s. Towhee
Savannah Sparrow
Grasshop'r Sparrow
Henslow's Sparrow
Vesper Sparrow
Slate-col. Junco
Tree Sparrow
Chipping Sparrow
Field Sparrow
Wh.-cr. Sparrow
Wh.-thr. Sparrow
Fox Sparrow
Lincoln's Sparrow
Swamp Sparrow
Song Sparrow
Lapland Longspur
Snow Bunting

SUGGESTED ABBREVIATIONS

S—Singing
M—Mating
N—Nest
N4E—4 eggs in nest
N4Y—4 young in nest
YO—Young out of nest

NOTES

Reports of:
(a) species not on this list, or
(b) species in the smaller type, or
(c) species outside of their usual season as specified in the B. O. S. Date Guide, 1965 edition, or
(d) species marked *, when observed outside of areas and dates indicated in the B.O.S. Date Guide, 1965 edition,

must be accompanied by written verifying details, preferably following the format of the B.O.S. Verification Form. Copies of this Form may be obtained free of charge from the B.O.S. Treasurer. The Date Guide, which may be purchased from the same source for fifty cents, should be consulted in regard to the verification requirements of all bird species known to have occurred in the Niagara Frontier Region.

REMARKS

This type of field check-list can be obtained from the museum nearest you.

Materials needed to make plaster casts.

Cardboard collar around the footprint.

Find a clear footprint of a bird.

Form a strip of cardboard into a circular collar and encircle the footprint by pushing the collar firmly into the ground. Hold the ends of the cardboard together with one of the paper clips.

Add plaster of Paris, a little at a time, to water in a paper cup until the mixture is about the same thickness as melted ice cream.

Add a pinch of salt and stir it in thoroughly. Salt will speed up the hardening process. Be careful not to add too much salt to the plaster or it will harden before you have time to pour it out of the cup. You will get used to the correct amount of salt to add after you have done it several times.

Pour the mixture into the collar surrounding the footprint. Smooth the plaster out to ensure that the back of the cast will be flat and even.

Take the second paper clip and bend it so that one of the rounded ends is sticking up. Insert the paper clip into the soft plaster. Since it will serve as a hook for your plaque, give some thought as to how you will want the print to be positioned when you hang it up later.

Leave the mixture until it has hardened. The amount of salt you put in will determine the number of minutes it takes to harden.

When it has hardened, remove the cardboard collar and carefully pry up the cast. Brush off the excess soil. Use water and the toothbrush to remove the remainder.

Boil the plaster cast in a solution of two parts water to one part borax. This will harden the plaster and help clean the plaque.

Paint the shape of the footprint, and then spray shellac over the cast.

Hang it on a wall when it has dried.

Make a collection of different footprints. Label them, and mount them on the wall.

Paint the footprint and its background different colours.

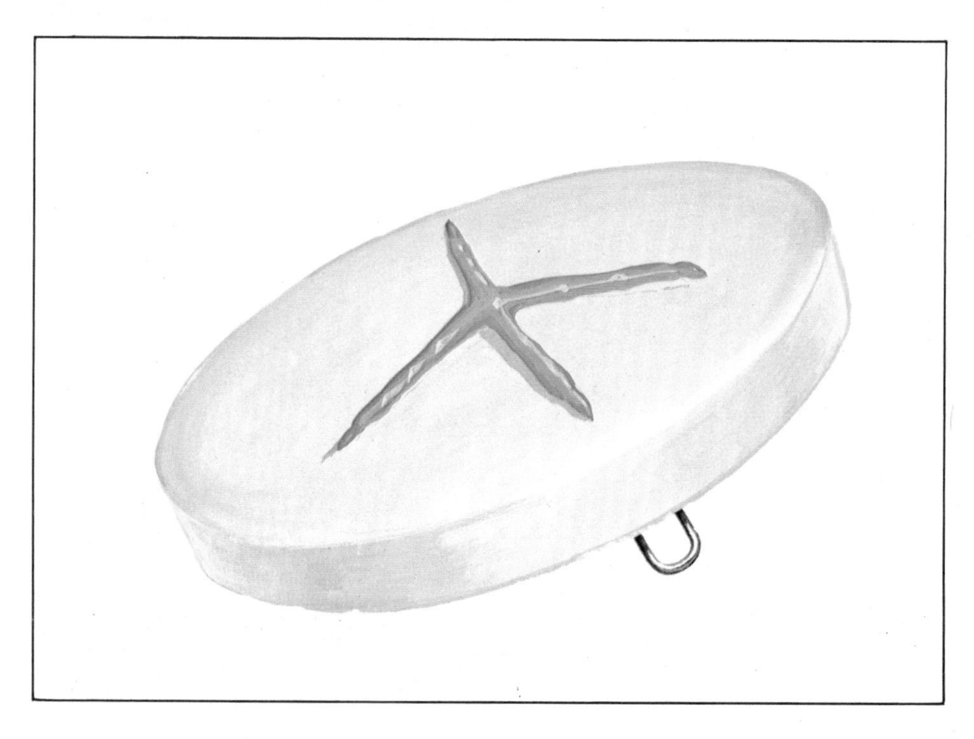

Digging Deeper

Why was the salt added?

What does the borax do for the plaster?

What other type of cardboard collar, other than circular, could you use?

Branching Out

Make plaster casts of the feet of dead birds.

Make plaster casts of birds' feathers.

What other activities can be done with live birds in the classroom?

Live birds for classroom use could come from the following sources: pet birds, such as budgies, canaries, pigeons from home; chickens from a farm; baby chicks hatched from an incubator.

Once a bird has been selected, the following activities could be carried out.

Weigh the amount of food and water the bird is given in a one week period.

At the beginning of the week record the bird's weight. At the end of the week record the bird's weight again. Does the bird show an increase in weight, the same weight, or a loss of weight? How does this relate to the total weight of food and water you gave the bird?

Weigh the bird every morning and every evening for one month. Graph your results.

Compare the body covering of the bird with the body covering of another animal, such as a cat.

Paint the bird's feet with tempera paint

and let it walk or hop over plain white mural paper. Discuss with the class what kind of measurements could be made of the bird's tracks. Compare the bird's tracks with tracks of other animals. How are they similar? different?

Place the bird on its back and watch what happens. Try the same activity with different birds. What happens? Why do they react the way they do?

Examine the bird's head to see if it has any ears.

Try to determine what the bird's angle of vision is. What problems will you have to consider in doing this activity? Do all birds have the same angle of vision? What would an owl's angle of vision be?

Plan a visit to a zoo to observe some of the rarer types of birds such as ostriches, penguins and tropical birds.

Establish your own, or a school, bird sanctuary. Name it after yourself or your school. What things should be in a bird sanctuary? What kind of protection would a bird sanctuary need? Visit or write to an established bird sanctuary if there is one in your area.

Set up your own aviary of pigeons (cock and hen). These birds are easily attainable from local pigeon fanciers. Some species are quite clean and can be kept in a cage 4 feet by 4 feet by 6 feet.

Birds' Eggs 2

2. Birds' Eggs

The study of eggs is called oology. Eggs are one of the most fascinating and colourful aspects of birds. The different sizes, shapes, colours and textures are as varied as the birds themselves. Eggs are about one-tenth the size of the adult bird, and while large birds tend to lay large eggs and small birds lay small eggs, there are exceptions. Birds whose young are fully developed and have feathers when they hatch, have larger eggs than those birds whose young are immature upon hatching. A baby bird which hatches helpless and nearly naked is called an *altricial* (al-trish-ill) bird. Most common birds are of this type. Some birds, such as chickens and pheasants, are born with down on their bodies and can walk around and feed themselves after hatching. These are *precocial* (pre-ko-shil) birds. Sometimes eggs are laid without a shell, only the inner membrane surrounds the eggs, yet the egg shape is still maintained. They are a common occurrence on chicken farms.

Eggs have a variety of unique external and internal properties which usually escape the casual observer's eye. For instance, of 18 eggs dropped onto the ground from the top of a 70 foot fireman's ladder at a school in England, only 3 broke. Incredible? Try Activity 4 if you don't believe it can be done. Many more delightful things can be discovered about eggs by handling and studying them carefully.

Ostrich egg, hummingbird egg and the dark emu egg—a study in contrast.

Activity 1:

What are the parts of a chicken's egg?

Buy a half dozen eggs.

Take one of the eggs, and being careful not to break the yolk, crack it open gently into a black frying pan or onto a piece of glass which has a black piece of paper under it. Make sure the surface onto which the egg is broken is level.

Examine the egg and the shell to see how many different parts you can discover.

Record your observations by means of a labelled diagram similar to the one shown.

Does your egg have these parts?

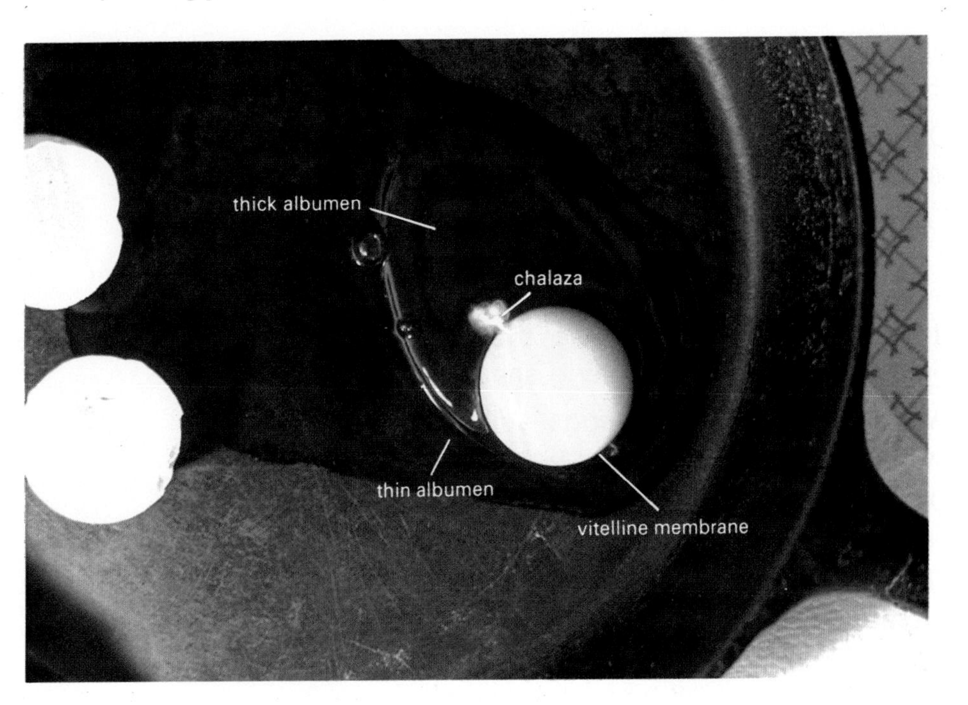

Digging Deeper

What different colours in the chicken's egg did you observe?

How many white, stringlike objects are attached to the yellow part of the egg? What are they called? What function do they serve?

What is the yellow part of the egg called?

There is a small white dot on the yellow part of the egg. What is it called? Why is it so very important?

Is the yellow part of the egg enclosed by a membrane or skin?

Is the yellow part of the egg the same colour all the way through?

What is the clear liquid surrounding the egg called? There are actually two clear liquids. One is thicker than the other. Which one is closer to the yellow part of the egg?

What is the texture (feel) of the egg shell?

Does the egg shell have a lining?

What is at the blunt, inside end of the egg shell?

What causes egg shells to be different colours?

Do other eggs have the same internal appearance?

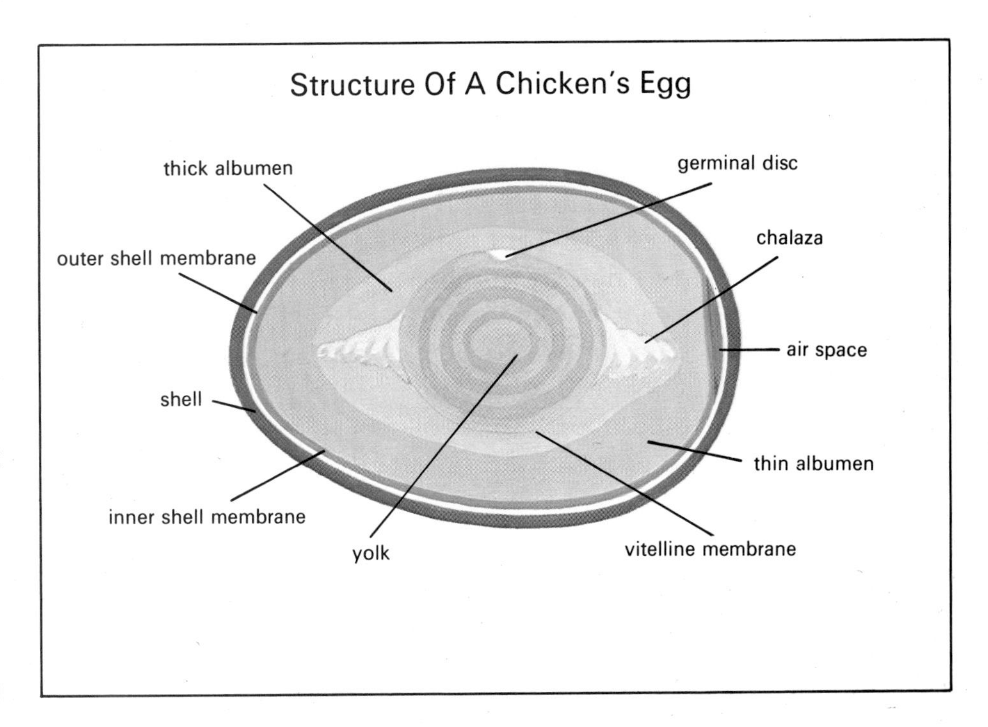

Branching Out

Boil an egg for 15 minutes. Peel it carefully, counting the layers beginning with the hard outer shell and continuing through to the centre.

Decode this formula: $CaCO_3$. The shell is composed of it.

Examine a piece of the egg shell under a microscope (100 magnification or more). Examine a piece of the membrane the same way. How does the chick breathe when it is in the egg shell?

Are the centres of *all* eggs yellow in colour?

Do all egg shells have the same texture as a chicken's egg?

Obtain the egg of a duck and the egg of a chicken. Cook the eggs by the same method and taste each one. Which one tastes better? Are all birds' eggs edible? Write to Dr. H. B. Cott of Cambridge University, England for his list of birds' eggs with their palatability (pleasant to the taste) rating. He and a *taste panel* have sampled and rated over 212 birds' eggs.

The set of eggs found in a bird's nest after incubation has started is called a *clutch*. Make a list of the names of some of the more common birds of your area. Beside each bird's name put the number of eggs it usually has in its clutch, i.e., robin—4. Use reference books to help you gather your data. What bird in your area lays the largest clutch? the smallest clutch? What is the interval of time between the laying of eggs? When will parent birds most readily desert their eggs, before incubation begins, during incubation, or when the eggs are about to hatch? During what part of the day do birds usually lay their eggs?

How many eggs are in this clutch?

Activity 2:

What measurements of a chicken's egg can be taken?

Buy a half dozen each of small, medium and large chicken eggs.

Obtain a weighing device, calipers, string, ruler (with millimetres).

Take one each of the small, medium and large eggs. Weigh each one separately and record its weight.

Weigh each set of six eggs, but first predict what their total weight will be.

Weigh just the contents of one of the eggs.

Eggs are sold in three sizes.

Weigh just the shell of the egg.

Use the calipers to discover the length and width of each egg. Record your measurements in millimetres in a chart like the one illustrated.

What is the length of this egg?

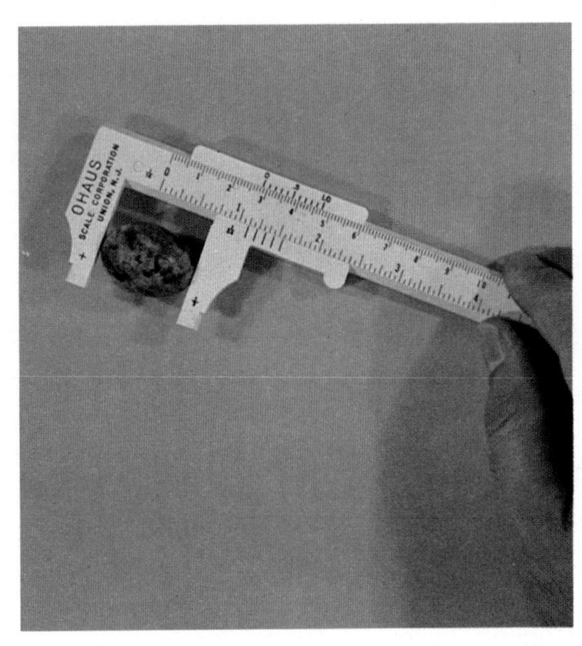

Use the string to measure the circumference on both the length and width of the egg. Record your measurements in millimetres.

EGG	SMALL		MEDIUM		LARGE	
	Length	Width	Length	Width	Length	Width
1						
2						
3						
4						
5						
6						
Average L and W						

Digging Deeper

What was the weight of the small egg? the medium egg? the large egg?

What is the average weight of a small egg? medium egg? large egg?

How much did the contents of the one egg weigh?

How much did the shell weigh?

How much would just the yolk weigh?

Is there much difference in length between a small and a large egg?

What does the term *Grade A Large* mean? How are eggs graded?

If one ostrich egg is equal to approximately two dozen large chicken eggs, about how much would the ostrich egg weigh?

How much larger usually is the long circumference than the short circumference?

Is there any relationship between the width of the egg and its short circumference? the length and its long circumference?

Branching Out

Does a hard-boiled egg weigh the same before and after it is boiled?

Try to discover from books which bird in your area lays the smallest egg, the largest egg.

If you know the cost of a dozen Grade A Large eggs, what is the cost per egg?

Boil the leftover eggs until they are very hard. Draw faces or designs on the shell of the egg. You could have a contest to see who can create the best face or design.

Bird's eggs can be identified with the help of a key. Colour and length are the main considerations in determining an egg's identity. The length should be measured with calipers correct to tenths of a millimetre. Contact a local ornithologist or your nearest science museum for assistance if you are interested in doing this particular activity. They will have keys and ideas that will help you. The following illustrations will aid in your attempts to name birds' eggs.

Some European people consider this an art.

Spotted sandpiper.

Short-eared owl.

Virginia rail.

Ruby-throated hummingbird.

Great blue heron.

Goldfinch.

Activity 3:

How can eggs be classified according to shape?

Almost everyone realizes what the term egg-shaped means, but actually eggs vary considerably in shape, depending upon the bird that laid them.

There are four basic classifications of egg shapes: spherical-elliptical (like the end of a spoon), subelliptical, oval, and pyriform (like a toy top). Within each set there are three variations. No bird lays a perfectly round or spherical egg, but some come very close. Try to roll a hen's egg in a straight line. What happens?

Study the chart on classification of egg shapes.

Classification Of Egg Shapes

Spherical-elliptical	Subelliptical	Oval	Pyriform
spherical	short subelliptical	short oval	short pyriform
elliptical	subelliptical	oval	pyriform
long elliptical	long subelliptical	long oval	long pyriform

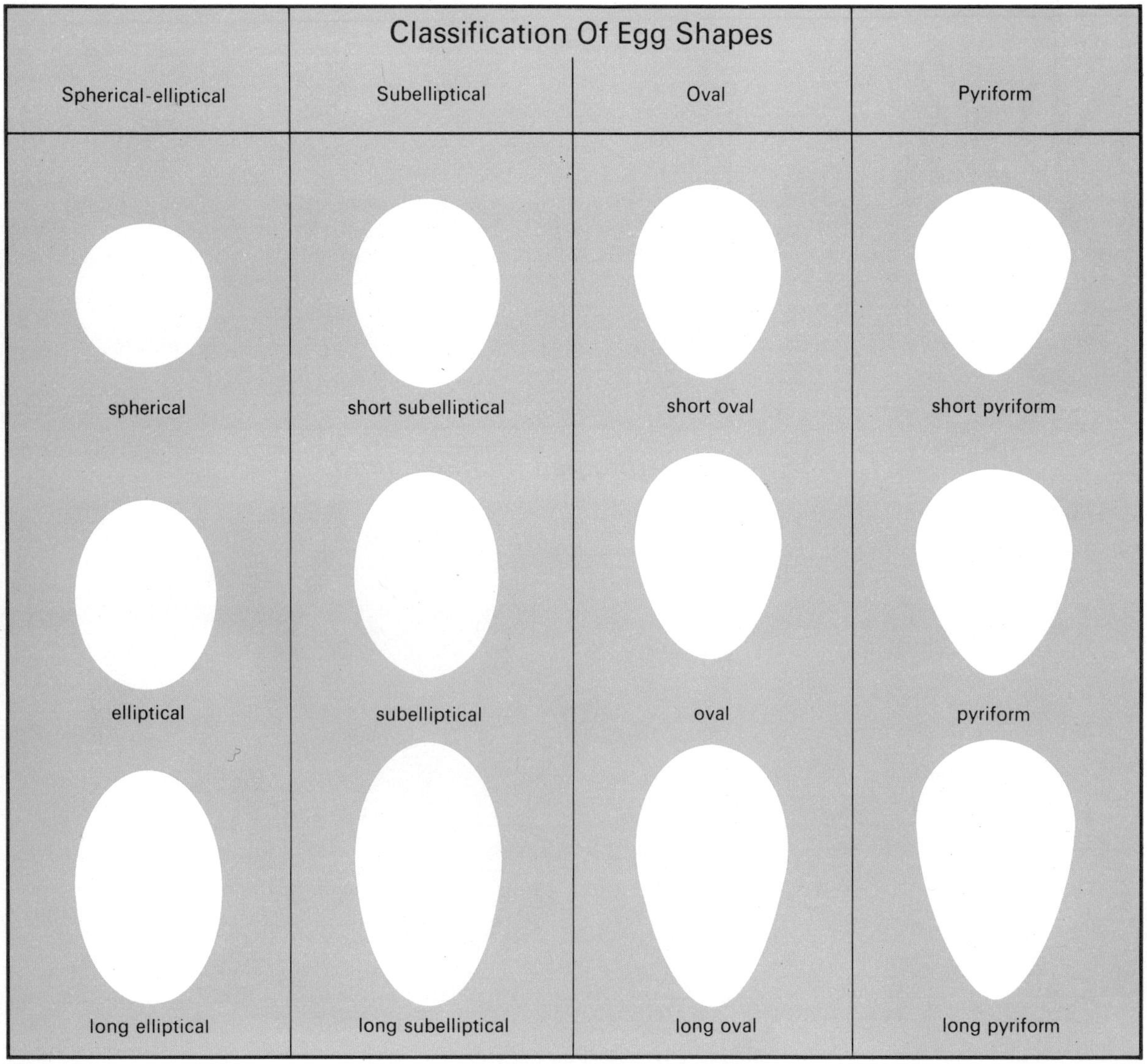

Using the chart, classify the above birds' eggs.

How would you classify this chicken's egg?

Digging Deeper

What is the most common shape of egg illustrated? the least common shape?

Which shape of egg would roll in a very tight circle? Do eggs have a built-in safety factor? If so, why?

Branching Out

Texture of egg shells is another property used in classifying eggs. Attempt to discover which birds have outstandingly rough textured egg shells and which have extremely smooth egg shells.

Make a picture collection of as many birds' eggs as you possibly can. Sort the pictures according to the shapes of the eggs.

Activity 4:

Under what conditions will a thrown egg break?

Some scientists believe that prehistoric birds actually laid their eggs while flying. Ridiculous you say? Almost everybody has learned from the experience of dropping an egg and cleaning up the mess, that eggs must be handled with great care. Do eggs always break when dropped? The truth is that they don't, even when dropped from great heights and at great speeds. The surface onto which the egg falls will determine to a great extent whether or not it will break.

Collect several dozen eggs.

Proceed to throw 12 eggs in a gentle arc onto a lawn, 12 onto concrete, and 12 into water.

Mr. Appleton throwing an egg from a fire ladder. One technique everyone is scrambling to adopt.

Keep an accurate record of what happens to the eggs thrown onto the different surfaces.

Many factors will have to be taken into consideration when doing this experiment; i.e., height, angle, number and size of eggs, spin, force.

Digging Deeper

How many eggs broke when thrown on the lawn? the concrete? the water?

Does the angle at which an egg is thrown onto a surface affect the number of breakages?

Would the shape of the egg influence its breakability?

Does the length of grass affect breakage?

Considering your findings, would it have

been possible for the ancestor of our modern-day chicken to have laid its eggs while in flight?

Branching Out

Test the strength of an egg. Hold an egg squarely between your hands (ends of the egg touching the palms) and press as hard as you can. The egg should be held straight and an even pressure applied to it. What happens? Hold an egg in one hand with your fingers around it, but don't dig your finger tips or thumb into the egg. Exert equal pressure on all sides of the egg. Now squeeze it as hard as you can. What happens?

See what you can find out about the elephant bird. Its egg contained about 2 gallons.

Make a list of egg puns; i.e., egged on, eggshausted.

What is the record number of eggs eaten at one sitting?

Activity 5(a):

How can a styrofoam pop cooler incubator be constructed?

One of the most rewarding experiences you can have while doing bird studies is to actually hatch eggs in an incubator. Hens' and ducks' eggs are easily obtained from local farmers or markets. The big hindrance is usually the lack of an incubator. This problem can be overcome either by buying a commercial incubator, borrowing one from an agricultural college, or constructing one yourself. A functional and simple type to construct is a styrofoam pop cooler incubator. Once your incubator is built you will have to learn how to operate it properly. Along with the incubator you will need a device for *candling* the eggs to determine whether or not they are fertile. This, too, is simple to construct.

A styrofoam pop cooler incubator.

In order to construct your homemade incubator you will have to obtain the following materials.

A complete *thermostat switch* for controlling the heat in the incubator, from a scientific supply house. Approximate cost is $5.00.

A rubber *pigtail socket* from a hardware store for about 65 cents.

A 40 or 60 watt *light bulb.* It will be the source of heat.

Three *marrettes* for connecting wires, from a hardware store for 25 cents.

A 6-foot piece of *lamp cord,* from a hardware store for 69 cents.

A *male plug,* from a hardware store at 20 cents.

A wall type *thermometer* for about 98 cents.

A *styrofoam pop cooler.* These can be purchased from large chain stores or hardware stores for about $1.50.

A piece of *hardware cloth,* 2 feet by 1 foot, from a hardware store for 35 cents.

A piece of *window glass,* 6 inches by 10 inches, from a hardware store for 25 cents.

Three 1-inch diameter *corks,* 15 cents.

Masking tape, 1 inch wide, 59 cents.

A piece of *burlap or cloth* to cover the hardware cloth.

The following tools will be needed.

A *steak knife,* to cut a window in the styrofoam, and to scrape insulation from the lamp cord wires.

A *pencil,* to make small holes in the styrofoam for the wires and thermostat.

Tin snips to cut the hardware cloth.

A *screwdriver* to connect the wires to the plug.

To construct your incubator use the following steps.

Cut an opening 4 inches by 8 inches in the side of the pop cooler for a window. The hole should be 1 inch smaller all around than the size of your glass.

Place the glass over the hole and tape it on with masking tape.

Use the point of the knife to make three air holes that the corks will fit. Space the holes below the window.

Make three pencil holes in the roof for the lamp cord wire, adjustment arm of thermostat, and support for pigtail light bulb.

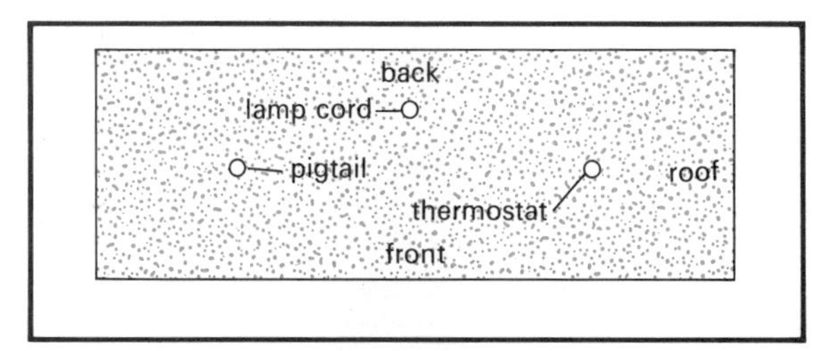

Diagram showing position of pencil holes.

Use the following diagram to connect the thermostat, socket, and lamp wires. Strip the ends of the wires bare first.

Diagram of how to wire the incubator.

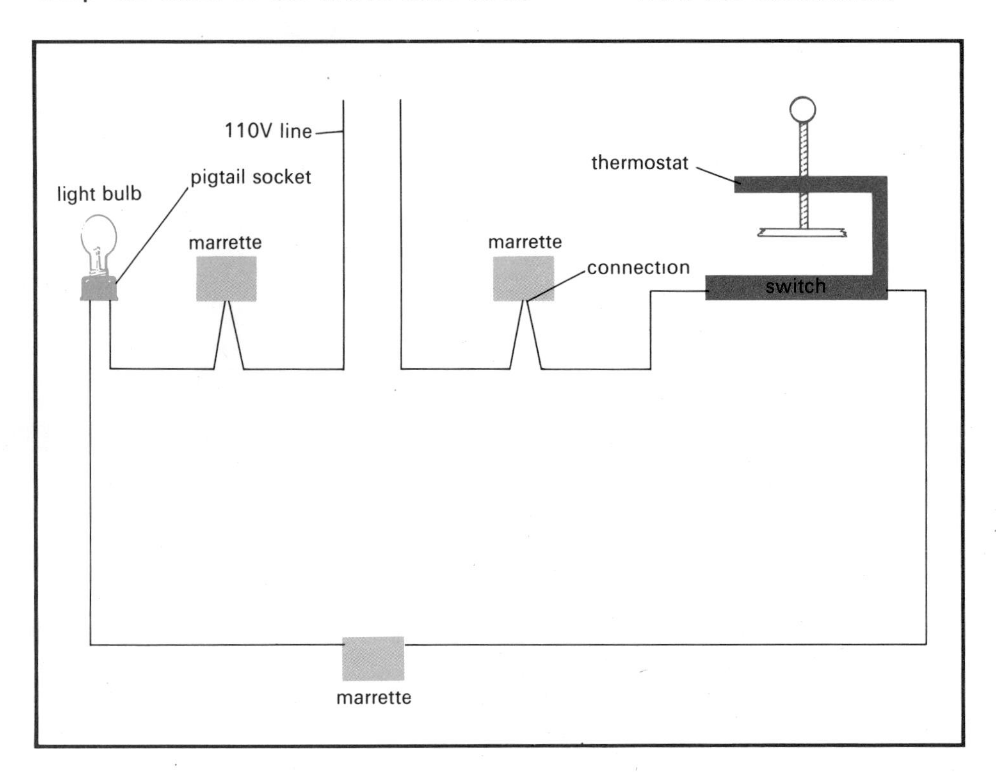

Cross sectional view of incubator roof.

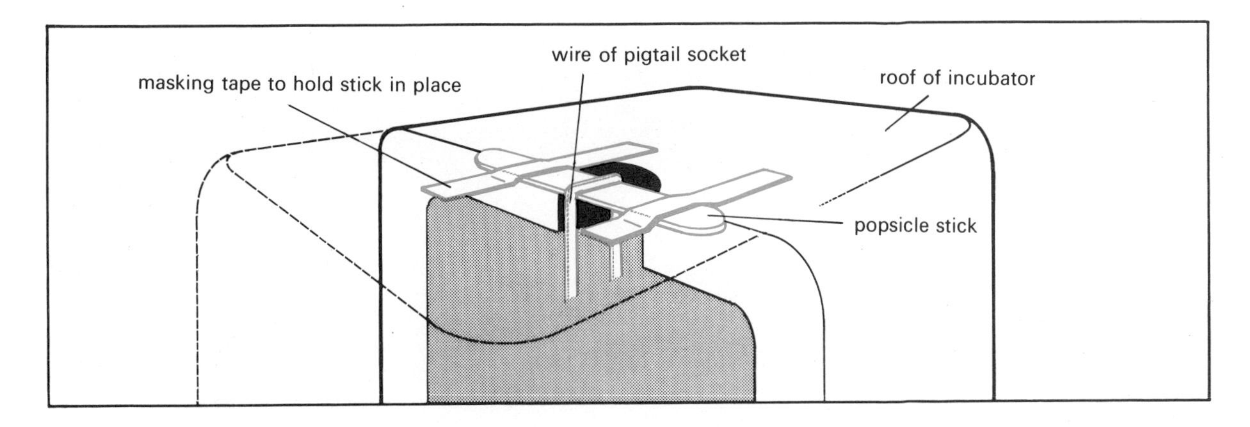

Cover all connections with marrettes which easily screw onto the wires.

Using the diagram as a guide, attach the thermostat and pigtail socket to the roof through the holes made with the pencil. Use tape and a popsicle stick on the outside to support the pigtail socket and light bulb.

Thread the lamp cord through the pencil hole near the back of the roof, strip the ends of the wire bare, and add the plug.

Bend the hardware cloth to make a support for the eggs.

Tape the thermometer onto the back inside wall of the incubator so that it can be easily read through the window.

Cover the hardware cloth with burlap or cloth.

To regulate your homemade incubator follow these steps.

Place a small container of water in the incubator.

Insert the corks into the holes (remove them only to regulate the humidity).

Adjust the thermostat control until a temperature of 101-103°F can be maintained for 2 or 3 days. This must be done before placing eggs in the incubator.

When the eggs are placed in the incubator allow plenty of time for the eggs and the incubator to regain a temperature of about 103°F. This should be achieved without adjusting the thermostat screw.

What is the average temperature for the 21 days?

Date	8 A.M.			4 P.M.			10 P.M.		
	Side up	Temp.	Moist.	Side up	Temp.	Moist.	Side up	Temp.	Moist.
Sept. 5	X	102°F	✓	O	103°F	✓	X	103°F	✓

SETTING THE EGGS

Fertilized eggs can usually be obtained from chick hatcheries, science supply houses, farms and local agricultural colleges. To obtain the eggs of other farmyard fowl, write to your provincial or state Agricultural Department and request the names of the producers of eggs you desire. For game bird eggs write to your provincial or state Department of Lands and Forests for names of producers.

Place the eggs on their sides in the incubator. Do not crowd them in. After the tray is filled, use a pencil to mark each egg so that none are missed when the eggs are turned. The thermometer must be positioned so that the bulb is level with the top of the eggs. Do not open the incubator the first day.

The eggs should be turned once the second day and three times a day after the second day until the twentieth day. Turning the eggs is best done by placing the palms of your hands on the eggs and rolling them around until you are sure all have been turned. After the twentieth day, do not turn the eggs. Learn to turn the eggs quickly to avoid chilling.

Water is placed in the incubator to prevent excessive drying out of the natural moisture in the egg. There is no set rule for supplying moisture. The important thing to watch is the air space in the end of the egg. When candling the eggs for fertility, note the size of the air space. If it is too large provide more moisture for the eggs.

Will all the eggs hatch? Why?

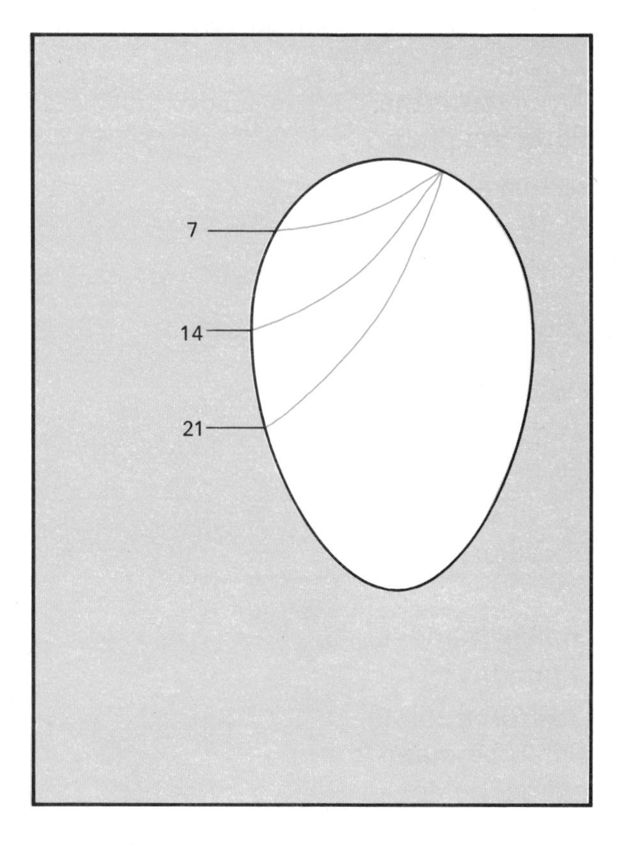

The size of the air space is the best guide to proper humidity. The diagram illustrates the proper air spaces at different stages of incubation, which is the effect of evaporation of water from the egg.

Activity 5(b):

How can an egg candler be constructed?

The eggs in your incubator should be tested for fertility. A candler or tester, as it is called, will enable you to determine whether or not an egg is fertile. If the eggs are fertile, a tiny dark spot with a net of little blood vessels will be seen floating inside the egg. This is the embryo. If the embryo has died, the blood will settle away from the centre towards the edges of the yolk. Some eggs may even be perfectly clear. All such eggs should be removed from the incubator. They can be hardboiled and later used for feeding the chicks. If you have white, clear shelled eggs, they can be candled on the third or fourth day. If the eggs are dark shelled, you will have to wait to the seventh or eighth day to test them.

A second fertility test should be made on the fourteenth day of incubation. All embryos which have died should be immediately removed.

Obtain a large coffee or juice can, an extension cord with a light bulb, a pair of duckbilled tin snips, and a spring-loaded clothes peg.

Remove one end from the tin can with a can opener.

Using the tin snips, cut a hole in the other end, large enough for the extension cord wire to go through.

In the side of the can cut a hole with a 1-inch diameter.

Remove the plug from the cord and thread it through the small hole in the end of the tin can. Then reattach the plug.

Pull the cord through the hole until the bulb is tight against it. Hold the bulb in that position by clamping the clothes peg onto the cord on the outside of the can.

Plug the extension cord in and candle your eggs.

An alternative to constructing a candler is to just use the beam of light from a film or filmstrip projector.

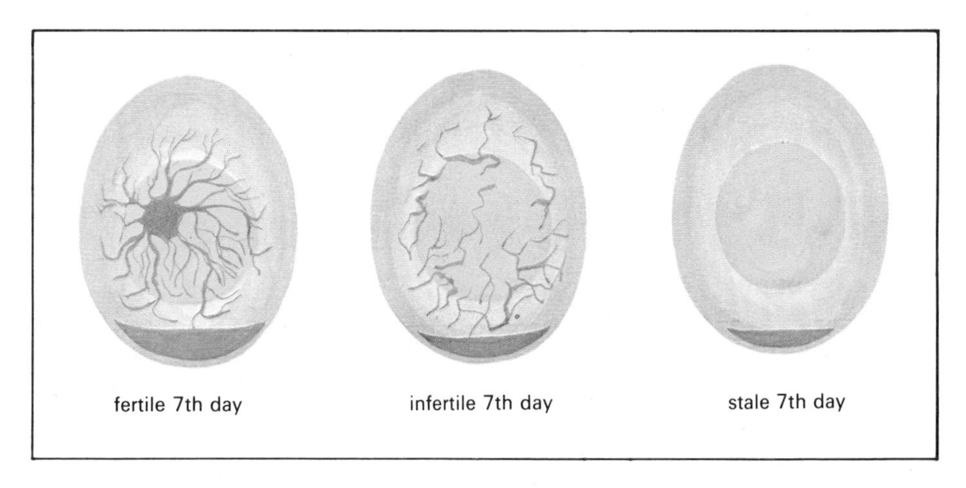

Diagram illustrates what could happen to the embryo after several days of incubation.

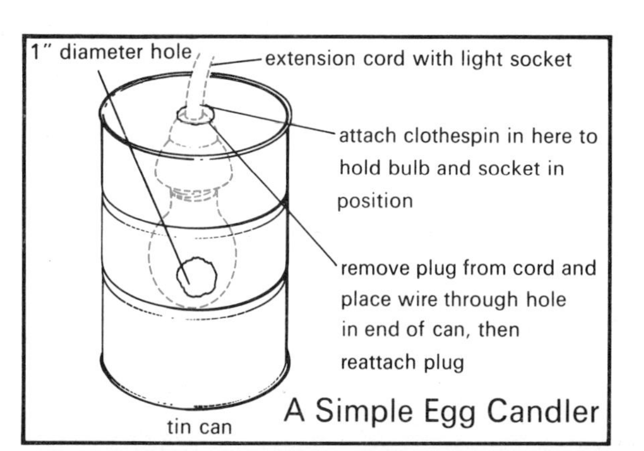

Diagram of a simple egg candler.

A beam of light from a filmstrip projector makes an excellent egg candler.

Digging Deeper

How many of the eggs were fertile?

Compare the air spaces in the eggs with the chart on page 36. Are the air spaces the proper size? How can you correct them if they are not?

How often should the eggs be candled?

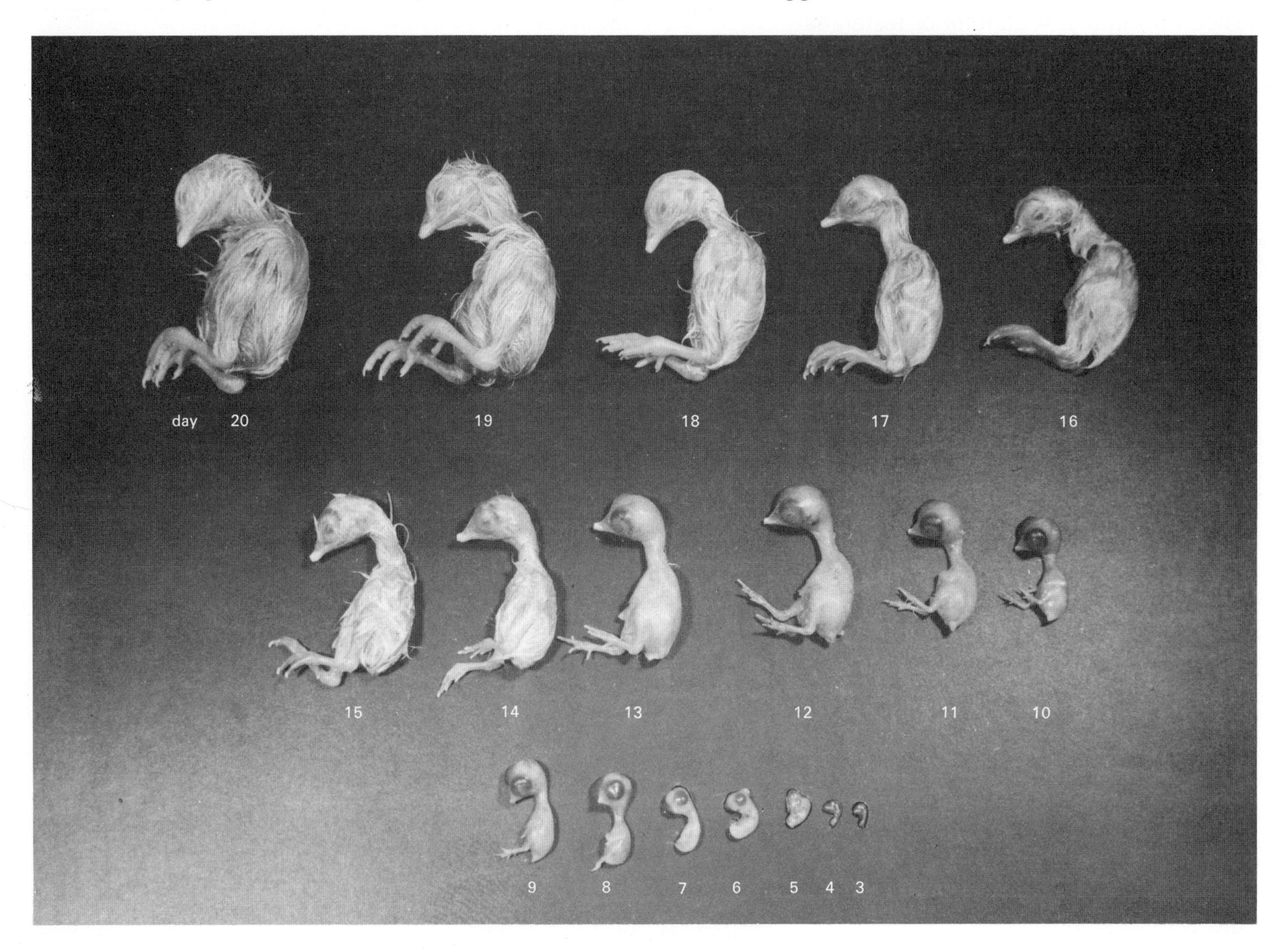

Development of the embryo over a period of 21 days.

Branching Out

Mark one side of the eggs with a pencil. Make an egg chart such as the one shown for turning the eggs.

	2 Turn over once	3 Turn 3	4 Turn 3	5 Turn 3	6 Turn 3	7 Turn 3
8 Turn 3	9 Turn 3	10 Turn 3	11 Turn 3	12 Turn 3	13 Turn 3	14 Turn 3
15 Turn 3	16 Turn 3	17 Turn 3	18 Turn 3	19 Turn 3	20 Wait	21 Wait

Put a window in an egg which candling has proven to be fertile.

With a pencil, draw a circle on the egg shell and cut around the circle with a razor blade.

Cut an X inside the circle, and using this as a starting point, pick off the shell bit by bit.

Put a square of saran wrap over the hole, and attach it with strips of adhesive tape.

Place the egg back in the incubator in a position in which the contents can be examined by looking through the window.

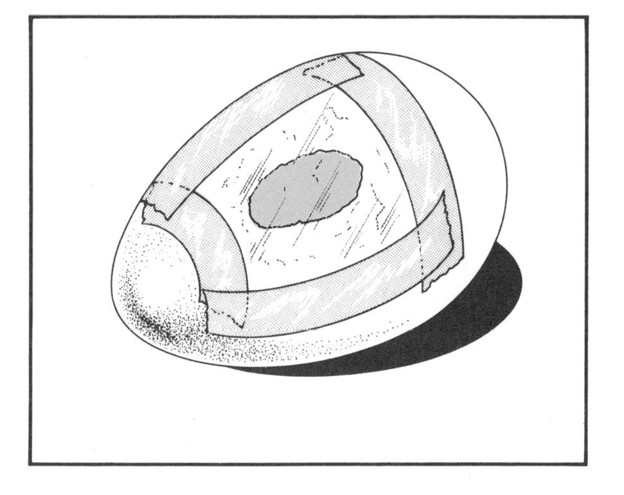

An egg with a window cut in it.

BREAKING OPEN SOME EGGS

After 36 and 48 hours of incubation and also when the embryo is 3, 7 and 14 days old, carefully remove one egg from the incubator, being careful not to turn it. Gently crack each egg and pour its contents into a bowl containing salt solution (1 teaspoon per quart of water) which has been warmed to the same temperature as the eggs in the incubator. There should be enough salt solution in the bowl to completely cover the embryo. With a hand lens you should be able to observe such phenomena as heartbeat and blood circulation, even in some of the earlier stages.

If you have the time and money to incubate a second batch of eggs, the following experiments could be tried.

Incubate one or two eggs at a temperature several degrees higher than normal. Compare the chick which hatches with a normally hatched chick.

Place an egg in a refrigerator or freezer at various stages of embryonic development and then return it to the incubator.

Apply a coating of wax over the entire surface of the egg shell. How does this affect embryo development?

At various stages of development, tape eggs to the outside edge of a phonograph turntable. Rotate at 78, 45, and

33⅓ rpm for various periods of time (always returning the eggs to the incubator).

Place eggs at various stages of development in different parts of a magnetic field. The field pattern can be found by sprinkling iron filings on a sheet of paper placed over the magnet. Use a strong magnet; vary the time of exposure.

Do not place dishes of water in the incubator. What is the effect of low humidity on embryo mortality?

Do not rotate the eggs. What happens?

Remember always to provide appropriate controls. If you remove eggs from the incubator for various periods, for example, to vary the environmental condition, you must also remove untreated eggs for the same periods. The more eggs you use, the more reliable your results will be.

Carefully weigh the eggs each day. Keep a record of any changes in weight.

Candle the eggs to see how the air space is changing from day to day.

MAKE A BROODER

Use the incubator as a home for the chicks for 24 to 36 hours. Remove the egg shells, and the cloth, and empty the water from the jar. Gradually decrease the temperature a few degrees each day until it corresponds to the temperature in the room.

Make a brooder from a small and a large cardboard box. To provide some heat for at least 2 days, place a 100 watt light bulb, attached to an extension cord, to one corner of the small box. Make openings in the small box so that the chicks can move in and out to the larger box which should contain a food trough and a water dispenser (jar turned upside down in a saucer). Line the bottom of both boxes with newspaper and change it regularly. Obtain some chick starter, a relatively inexpensive prepared food, from a feed store.

Observe and record how the size and colour of the feathers change from day to day.

Birds' Nests 3

3. *Birds' Nests*

Nidology, the study of birds' nests, can reveal many hidden facts about birds' habits, nesting territories, materials used in nest construction, eggs, and mating habits.

The best time to collect nests is during the autumn when the leaves have fallen. Since most birds build an entirely new nest each year there is no harm in collecting old nests. However, the eggs of most wild birds are protected by law! A collection of different types of nests will be valuable for the activities which follow in this chapter. When gathering nests, follow these guidelines.

(a) Always ask for permission to explore private property.

(b) If the nest rests upon a branch, cut off the branch (get permission to do this).

(c) If the branch can't be removed or the nest rests upon something else, i.e., the ground or a wall, remove the nest carefully and place it in a plastic bag.

(d) Leave occupied nests alone!

(e) Store collected nests in cardboard boxes or mount them on a wall or stand.

(f) All nests should be sprayed with an insecticide, such as *Raid*, to slow down the deterioration of the nest.

(g) Label each nest to show the bird that built it, where it was found, when it was found, and the name of the person who found it.

(h) Keep only nests which are in very good condition.

Is this nest labelled correctly?

Nest mounted on a wall shelf.

A branch from a tree can be used as a base to mount nests on.

Nests come in all shapes and sizes, ranging from floating nests on water, to underground nests in banks and cliffs. Some common types of nests are pensile (hanging like a pendulum), semipensile (hanging but with much more support), platform, saucer, saddled, domed and cupped.

Platform—mourning dove.

Saddled—hummingbird.

Semi-pensile—red-eyed vireo.

Cupped—robin.

Pensile (hanging)—Baltimore oriole.

Survey the nests in your locality. Which is the most common type of nest? the least common? Use a bar graph similar to the one shown to record your findings.

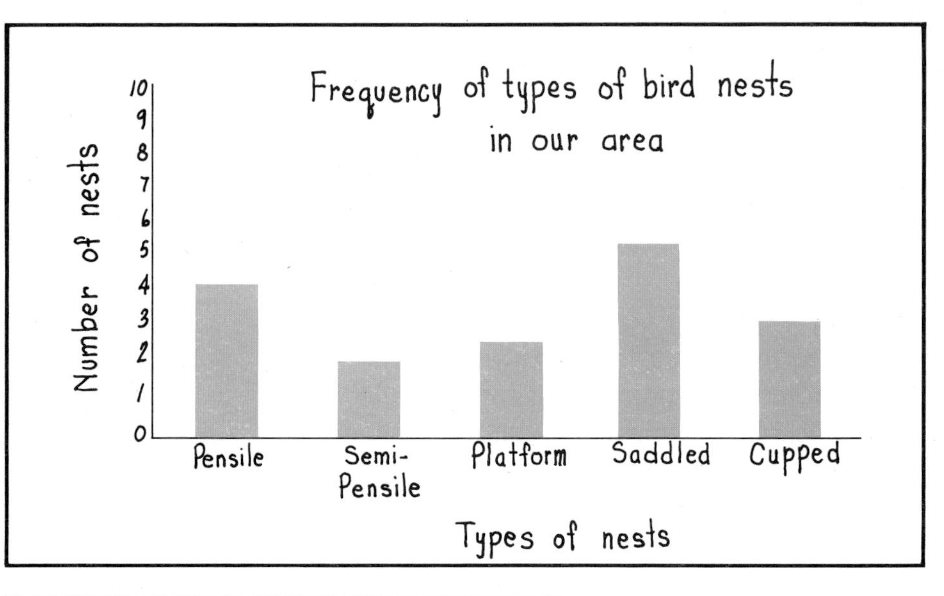

Activity 1:

Do birds build their nests on any particular side of a tree?

Obtain a magnetic compass, a clipboard and some paper on which to record your data. Your data sheet might look similar to the one in the photograph.

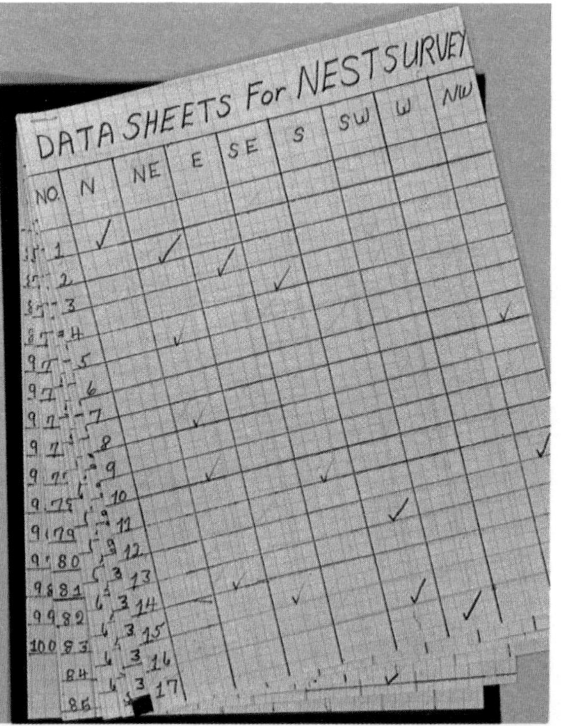

Data collection sheet for bird nest survey.

Survey as many trees with nests as possible in as wide an area as you can. At least 100 trees with nests over several acres of land or several city blocks should be examined.

To determine on which side of the tree the nest is located, stand next to the trunk of the tree with the magnetic compass in your hand so that your back is to the trunk and you are facing the nest. Orient the compass by turning it until N on the needle is in line with the letter N on the compass rose. Look at the nest and decide which side of the tree it is on.

Display your data in the form of a graph.

You could also record your data in a diagram like the one shown.

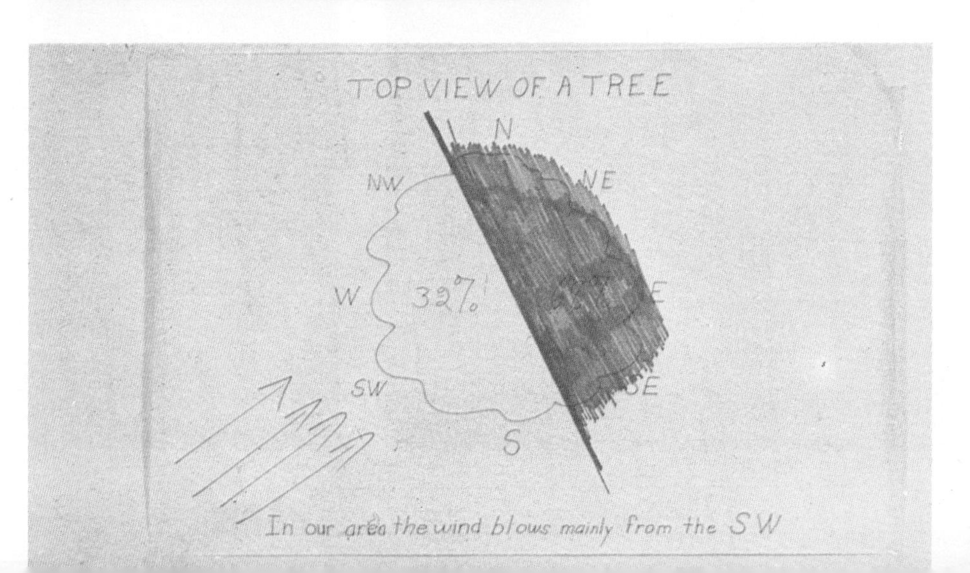

Digging Deeper

On which side of the trees were the most nests found? the least?

From what direction does the prevailing

A hypsometer is a special type of angle finder which gives a direct measurement of height.

wind blow in your area? Is there any relationship between the direction of the wind and the nests?

How many different types of nests, i.e., pensile, saddled, cupped, did you observe in your survey?

Of the nests that you surveyed, where were the nests located, near the ends of the branches or nearer the trunk of the tree?

Branching Out

Survey just pensile nests to discover whether or not birds which build that particular type of nest do build on the side of the tree opposite the prevailing winds of the area.

Does a particular species of bird, i.e., yellow warbler, build its nests on any particular side of a tree?

Find several nests which belong to the same species of bird and, using a clinometer, calculate their average height above the ground. Would your answer be an accurate one? Do birds of a species build their nests a specific distance above the ground?

Record your data in a chart like the one illustrated.

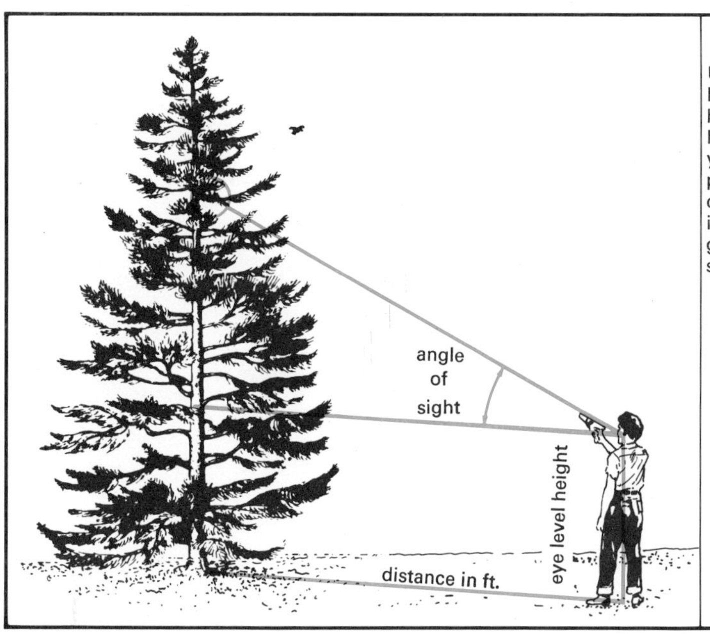

Use graph paper (vertical axis—*Height in ft.* and horizontal axis—*Distance in ft.)* to calculate the height of the nest. Place the protractor along the horizontal axis with the centre on the number of feet you were away from the nest. Draw a line from that point, through the angle you measured with the clinometer, to the height scale. The height of the nest is obtained by adding the numeral obtained from the graph where the angle of sight line cuts the height scale, and the eye level height.

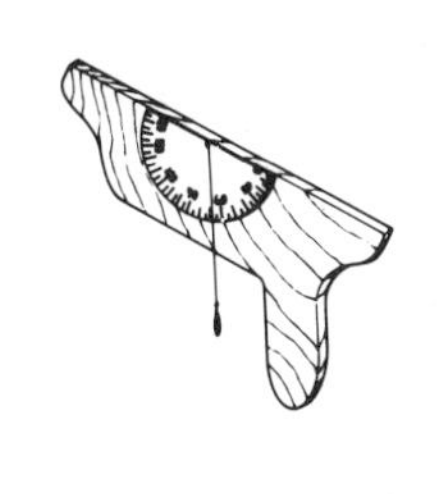

A clinometer measures the angle between your eye and the nest. If you know the angle and the distance you are away from the nest, the height of the nest can be easily calculated.

Activity 2:

In how many ways can a bird's nest be measured?

This activity will require you to have the following equipment: scales for weighing, string, ruler calibrated in inches and centimetres, and a pair of calipers.

Collect several nests made by the same type of bird, i.e., robins' nests.

Weigh the nests and record your answers in ounces and in grams.

Measure the depth of the cups or pockets of the nests with the ruler. Give your answers in inches and in millimetres.

Using the calipers, measure the thickness of the nests' walls. Measure the nests' inside and outside diameters. Record your measurements in both English and metric units.

How much does this nest weigh?

Use a long piece of string to measure the distance around the outside of the nest (circumference). Record your findings in inches and in millimetres.

Circumference is the distance around the nest.

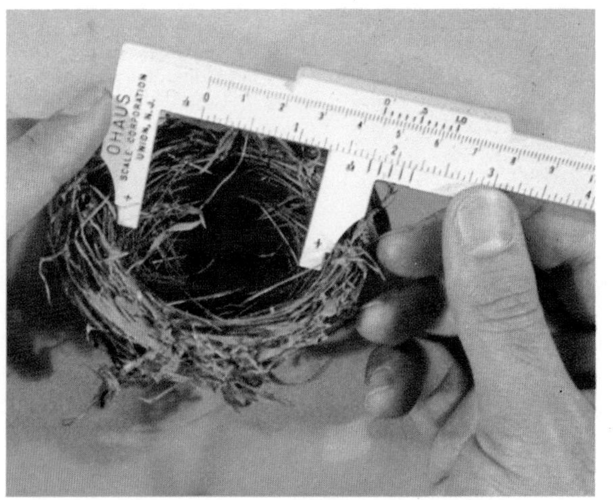

When using a key to identify a nest the inside diameter is very important.

How wide is this nest?

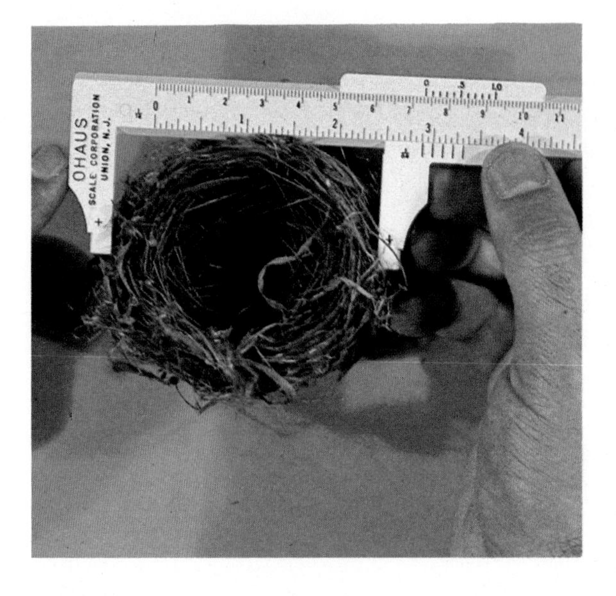

What other measurements could you take?

Display all your findings in a table such as the one shown.

Nest	1	2	3	4	5	6	7	8	Remarks
Weight									
Depth									
Diameter (inside)									
Diameter (outside)									
Circumference									
Other									

Digging Deeper

Did all the nests have approximately the same measurements?

Is there any relationship between the circumference of a nest and its diameter?

Estimate the weight of the bird that built the nest. How could you check your answer?

Is there any relationship between the height of the bird and the depth of its nest cup?

Compare the inside diameters of all the nests. Is there much variation?

Branching Out

Collect the nests of different species of birds in your area and set up a comparative table showing their different measurements.

From reference books dealing with birds try to discover which bird builds the largest nest, the smallest nest.

What is the largest bird's nest found in your area? the smallest?

Collect and compare the nests found in trees and in bushes to the nests found in marshes, in banks, on the ground and in holes in trees.

A very special relationship exists between the location of a nest and the bird. This special relationship might be explored under the following headings: nesting materials; food; habitat, such as farmland, woodlot, swamp, town; body structure; type of shelter; hiding places; numbers of birds observed.

Make a list of habitats and the birds found in each, for example, swamp or marsh—red-wing blackbird.

Many places serve as nesting locations. Make a list of actual nesting sites and the species of bird, i.e., tree branches—robin; holes in ground—kingfisher; buildings (outside)—sparrow.

Activity 3:

What materials are found in a bird's nest?

Birds have been known to use almost every material available in building their nests. Such items as electric light bulbs, cigar boxes, automobile parts, rubber tires and other trash have been found in some eagles' nests. Examining materials found in birds' nests can be an interesting experience. F. H. Herrick's book, *Wild Birds at Home,* gives an excellent description of birds' nests and how different species of birds build them.

Obtain a small, typical, cup-shaped nest and proceed to take it apart piece by piece.

If the nest you select is held together with mud, soak it in a pail of water before taking it apart.

Classify or sort the material in the nest into groups and label each accordingly, i.e., bark, moss, twigs, mud.

Make a display of all the materials you found in the nest. Remember a good display has a title, labels on all its parts and eye appeal.

Digging Deeper

How many different types of material did you find in the nest?

What type of material was most common? least common?

Do all birds' nests contain the same type of materials?

Were the materials found on the outside of the nest the same as those found in the lining of the nest?

What is the one main reason birds build nests?

A nest material board.

Branching Out

In early spring make a nest material board. When it is completed hang it on a fence or in a tree. A nest material board is simply a piece of perforated masonite with pieces of string, thread, yarn and shreds of cloth pulled through the holes. Examine the board regularly to see which items are missing. Which is the most popular material? least popular?

Make a list of the birds in your area which don't make nests.

Make a list of the birds in your area which make nests but do not collect materials to build it.

Make a list of the birds in your area which nest singly, and in colonies.

Activity 4:

How many pieces of material are used in the construction of a bird's nest?

To carry out this activity obtain a small cupped or platform nest made mainly of grass and twigs, i.e., sparrow's nest.

Take the nest apart carefully piece by piece. Try not to snap or break any of the strands of grass or the twigs. Work slowly and patiently.

Once you have separated all the pieces, count the total number of individual parts.

Digging Deeper

How many individual pieces of material were in the nest?

How many trips do you think it took the bird to make the nest?

Are all the pieces approximately the same weight and length?

How were the pieces held together?

Was there any order as to how the materials were put into the nest, i.e., heavier materials on the bottom, lighter materials on top?

Branching Out

What are some of the factors that would determine the location of a bird's nest?

Classify or group the parts of the nest into subsets using length of individual pieces as the basis for grouping. Does the bird seem to prefer any particular length of material? What was the longest length of material? the shortest length?

Lay the pieces of the nest end to end in the school hallway. How far do they stretch? Measure the distance in feet. Do all nests tend to stretch that far?

In early spring try to observe birds building nests. Do both male and female help in building it? Approximately how long does it take to build the nest from start to finish? How soon after the nest is finished are the eggs laid? Are all the eggs laid on the same day? Are there any birds which begin laying their eggs before the nest is finished?

Sort the materials you find in a nest into groups.

A nesting shelf.

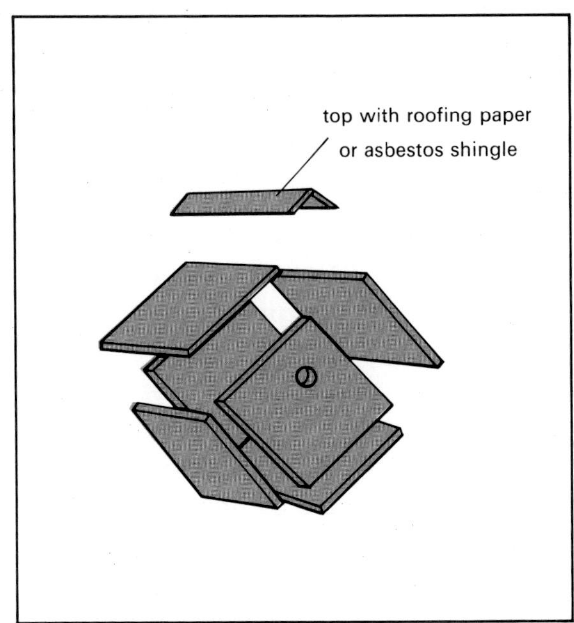

Simple wren house.

Nail keg wood duck house.

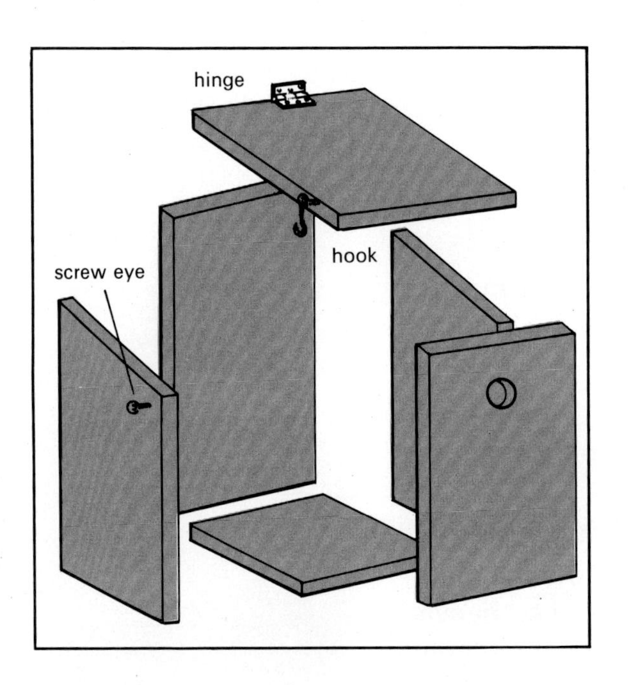

Basic plan for simple birdhouse. Vary dimensions to suit species desired.

Activity 5:

What type of birdhouses can be built?

You could build several different types of homes if you have the time, materials and tools.

The measurements you need to build homes for several kinds of birds are shown in the table.

Digging Deeper

How are *nesting boxes* different from birdhouses?

What animals might disturb birdhouses? How could this be prevented?

Measurements Of Nest Boxes For Common Species

Species	Entrance diameter (Box size)	Width	Depth	Height above ground
House wren	1″	2½″	6″	6′
Chickadee Nuthatch Downy woodpecker	1¼″	3⅛″	8″	8′
Bluebird English sparrow Tree swallow	1½″	4″	10″	10′
Red-headed woodpecker	1¾″	4⅜″	11″	11′
Starling Crested flycatcher Hairy woodpecker	2″	5″	12½″	13′
Flicker	2½″	6″	15″	15′
Screech owl Sparrow hawk	3″	7½″	19″	19′
Wood duck Hooded merganser Common goldeneye	*(3″ x 4″)	10″	25″	25′

*Elliptical opening to prevent access by raccoons is preferable.

Nest boxes.

An exploded view of the four-sided slab nest box. All the sides are nailed to the base and to each other. The removable, square lid is nailed to the top. If made from dressed lumber the nest box should have a sloped roof.

Activity 6:

How can birds' nests be identified?

"What bird built that nest?", is a familiar question which usually cannot be answered. Of all the hundreds of thousands of bird experts in the world only a few would be able to identify a bird's nest without the aid of a written key and even then it may still prove too difficult.

The science of using a key to identify birds' nests is not very exact, because sometimes the birds will fool you. Written keys for nests are about 85 percent accurate.

A key is a tool just like a microscope and if used with care and patience can enable you to discover the identity of an unknown nest. This particular key is limited to the more common types of nests found in Northeastern U.S.A. and Canada. If you do not live in this area, write or visit your local museum. They can probably recommend a suitable key for your area, i.e., *Key to the Nests of Pacific Coast Birds,* by E. Stevenson.

Some nests can be named in 5 minutes while other nests may take as long as 20 to 40 minutes. Some nests may even require you to get the help of an expert before its final identity can be known. Don't rush through the key, take your time and read carefully. Use a more sophisticated key with illustrations (*Birds' Nests: A Field Guide*, by Richard Headstorm) if one is available to help you confirm your final decision. For positive identification of a nest, attempt to identify the adult bird while it is actually on the nest.

The key that follows is practical for nests which are in good condition. It has two parts. The first part, or the *Major Key,* has capital letters in front of the statements and the second part, the *Minor Key,* uses Roman numerals.

All good keys are alternate, that is, you can take one of two routes. At first, the two routes show big differences but later the differences become very hard to detect, and you must read very carefully to obtain the correct answer.

To begin the identification of a nest, determine in the Major Key the division in which a nest belongs, then turn at once to that division in the Minor Key and trace it through. Whenever the letter heading, a part of the key, is doubled or trebled, it indicates the alternative conditions. After determining the alternative which best fits the nest, the other statements are ignored and the tracing is continued.

Read the following steps.

(a) Examine the entire key to familiarize yourself with its organization.

(b) Read through the divisions of the Major Key, i.e., A to JJ.

(c) Decide on the division which best suits your nest, i.e., A, AA, AAA, or C, CC, etc.

(d) Once the division has been selected read the Roman numeral at the extreme right-hand side of the page; then proceed to that section in the Minor Key, i.e., if the division is B in the Major Key the Roman numeral is III, you go to section III in the Minor Key.

(e) Begin reading the letter headings at the left-hand side of the page. Select which letter heading is most appropriate for your nest and continue tracing. (Section 1 of the key is the only section which doesn't have letter headings. Just read the 4 headings in bold type and select the most suitable one.) If the nest's category doesn't fall under any of the letter headings, i.e., A, AA, go to the B's, or if necessary the C's or D's. Continue tracing through the alternatives until a correct answer is reached.

KEY TO THE NESTS OF THE COMMON SUMMER-RESIDENT BIRDS OF NORTHEASTERN NORTH AMERICA

MAJOR KEY

A. On the ground or in tussocks of grass I
AA. In burrows in the ground II
AAA. Above ground, in bushes or trees, on cliffs, or about buildings
- B. Hanging or semipensile nests III
- BB. Not hanging
  - C. In holes in trees or in bird-boxes IV
  - CC. Not in holes
    - D. Containing sticks or large twigs V
    - DD. With no sticks
      - E. Felted, nests of cottony materials, not lichen-covered VI
      - EE. Lichen-covered, or not felted
        - F. Containing an inner layer of mud VII
        - FF. With no mud
          - G. Covered with lichens VIII
          - GG. With no lichens
            - H. Mostly of bark, fibers and rootlets, with or without horsehair lining IX
            - HH. Mostly of grasses, rootlets, straws, and leaves; usually with horsehair in the lining
              - J. Not spherical X
              - JJ. Spherical XI

MINOR KEY

I. ON THE GROUND OR IN TUSSOCKS OF GRASS—These nests are seldom found except when occupied and then can be identified by the birds. Only a list will be given. (See also Spherical.)

IN FIELDS—Bobolink, bobwhite, field sparrow, grasshopper sparrow, horned lark, killdeer, meadow lark, nighthawk, pheasant, Savannah sparrow, song sparrow, spotted sandpiper, vesper sparrow.

IN WOODS—Black-and-white warbler, brown thrasher, Canadian warbler, hermit, thrush, junco, Louisiana water thrush, mourning warbler, ovenbird, ruffed grouse, song sparrow, towhee, veery, water thrush, whippoorwill, woodcock.

IN MARSHES—Bittern, black duck, black tern, coot, Florida gallinule, king rail, loon, marsh hawk, Maryland yellow throat, pied-billed grebe, short-eared owl, sora rail, swamp sparrow, Virginia rail, Wilson's snipe.

II. IN BURROWS IN THE GROUND

A. Nesting in colonies in sandbanks.................................Bank swallow
AA. Nesting singly
  B. Drilling its own burrow......................................Kingfisher
  BB. Utilizing some other burrow........................Rough-winged swallow

III. HANGING OR SEMIPENSILE NESTS

A. In reeds or swamp bushes
  B. Open above
    1. A platform; only slightly hollowed.........................Least bittern
    2. Deeply hollowed...............................Red-winged blackbird
  BB. Spherical nests, opening on side............Long and short-billed marsh wrens

AA. **In upland bushes and trees**
  B. Small, less than 2 inches deep inside; fully suspended
    1. In berry bushes....................................White-eyed vireo
    2. In low branches or saplings..........................Red-eyed vireo
    3. In evergreens (usually)............................Blue-headed vireo
    4. In middle of tree.............................Yellow-throated vireo
    5. In tree top or outer branches..........................Warbling vireo
  BB. Small; semipensile, partially supported..................Acadian flycatcher
  BBB. Larger, over 2 inches deep inside
    1. Of dried grasses; sometimes partially supported.............Orchard oriole
    2. Of fibers, strings and the like.........................Baltimore oriole

IV. IN HOLES IN TREES OR IN BIRD-BOXES

A. Nesting in colonies...Purple Martin
AA. Nesting singly
  B. Drilling holes; no nest at bottom
    1. Opening about 1½"............................Downy woodpecker
    2. Opening about 1¾"..............................Hairy woodpecker
    3. Opening about 2"..........................Red-headed woodpecker
    4. Opening over 2"..Flicker

BB. Using old woodpecker holes, or natural cavities of the same size, or birdhouses with similar openings; building a nest at bottom of cavity
1. Nest of sticks, lined with feathers.......................... House wren
2. Nest entirely of grasses...................................... Bluebird
3. Nest of straws and feathers
a. Nest cuplike, open above............................ Tree swallow
b. Nest spherical or partially arched............. House (English) sparrow
4. Nest of fibers, moss, wool and feathers............ Chickadee and nuthatch
5. Nest usually containing a cast snake skin............... Crested flycatcher
BBB. Using larger natural cavities...... Barred owl, great horned owl, and wood duck

V. CONTAINING STICKS OR LARGE TWIGS

A. Bulky nests in trees 15 to 60 inches outside diameter
1. Very large, 30 to 60 inches......................... Fish hawk and bald eagle
2. Smaller, no lining; flat.. Heron
3. Hollowed; lining of bark............... Crow, long-eared owl, great horned owl
4. Hollowed, lining of fresh leaves or evergreens.. Hawks (Red-shouldered, Red-tailed, Cooper's, Sharp-shinned)
5. Spherical nests.. (Squirrel)
AA. Smaller nests, less than 15 inches outside
B. Cuplike; in chimneys, hollow trees or silos.................. Chimney swifts
BB. Otherwise
C. Platform; very shallow
1. No lining.. Mourning dove
2. A little lining... Cuckoo
CC. Deeply hollowed, 1 to 3 inches deep
D. In thickets or scrubby trees; under 3½ inches inside diameter
1. Lining of leaves and rootlets
a. Over 3 inches inside........................ Brown thrasher
b. 3 inches or less................................. Catbird
2. Lining of bark and wool....................... Migrant shrike
DD. In trees, usually evergreen; over 3½ inches inside diameter .... Blue jay

VI. FELTED NESTS OF COTTONY MATERIAL

A. Nests wider than high; containing thistledown........................ Goldfinch
AA. Nests higher than wide; no thistledown
B. Thick-walled; usually in vertical fork of bush or tree........... Yellow warbler
BB. Thick-walled; usually on horizontal branch of apple or similar tree; usually decorated with bits of paper.................................. Least flycatcher
BBB. Thin-walled; usually close to trunk of small sapling................. Redstart

VII. CONTAINING AN INNER LAYER OF MUD

A. Built in trees
  B. Of grasses and mud, usually no moss nor dead leaves
    1. Under 4 inches inside diameter . . . . Robin
    2. Over 4 inches inside diameter . . . . Bronzed grackle
  BB. Containing dead leaves and usually moss . . . . Wood thrush
AA. Built on buildings, bridges or cliffs
  B. Outer layer of grasses, mud within
    1. Under 4 inches inside diameter . . . . Robin
    2. Over 4 inches inside diameter . . . . Bronzed grackle
  BB. Outer layer of mud, some grasses
    1. Open at top, cup-shaped . . . . Barn swallow
    2. Open at side, gourd-shaped . . . . Cliff swallow
  BBB. Outer layer of moss and mud . . . . Phoebe

VIII. WITH AN OUTER COVERING OF LICHENS; SADDLED ON BRANCH

A. Very small, less than 1½ inches outside diameter . . . . Ruby-throated humming bird
AA. Larger, over 1½ inches outside diameter
  1. Very deep, over 1½ inches. . . . . Blue-gray gnat catcher
  2. Shallow, under 1½ inches . . . . Wood pewee

IX. MOSTLY OF BARK, FIBERS, AND ROOTLETS, WITH OR WITHOUT HORSEHAIR LINING

A. Small woodland nests, usually in evergreens; less than 2 inches in diameter (seldom found) . . . . Pine warbler, Magnolia warbler, black-throated green warbler, purple-finch, Blackburnian warbler.
AA. Small woodland nests, less than 2 inches in diameter; usually in bushes or sprouts
  1. No dead wood in bottom . . . . Chestnut-sided warbler
  2. Bits of dead wood in bottom. . . . . Black-throated blue warbler
AAA. Orchard or woodland nests, over 2 inches inside diameter
  B. Usually thin, flimsy structures
    1. Little or no lining; usually in high bushes . . . . Rose-breasted grosbeak
    2. Considerable lining; usually in trees . . . . Scarlet tanager
  BB. Thick, well-formed structures; with some cotton or wool
    1. Shallow, about 1 inch deep . . . . Kingbird
    2. Deeper, about 1½ inches deep . . . . Cedar waxwing

X. MOSTLY OF GRASSES, ROOTLETS, STRAWS, AND LEAVES; USUALLY WITH HORSEHAIR IN THE LINING, AND NOT SPHERICAL

A. With many leaves; placed in weeds, ferns, or low bushes
  B. Under 2 inches inside diameter . . . . Indigo bunting
  BB. Over 2 inches inside diameter
    1. Nest placed on mat of leaves . . . . Veery
    2. Leaves woven into nest . . . . Yellow-breasted chat
AA. With few or no leaves
  B. Less than 1¾ inches inside diameter
    1. With thick horsehair lining . . . . Chipping sparrow
    2. With few hairs or none . . . . Field sparrow
  BB. Over 2 inches inside diameter
    1. With many or few hairs in lining . . . . Song sparrow
    2. No hairs, a few leaves . . . . Yellow-breasted chat

XI. SPHERICAL NESTS OF GRASSES, BARK, OR FIBERS

A. On the ground; very thickly lined with soft grasses . . . . (Meadow mouse)
AA. In bushes or vines, usually on some old bird's nest, and lined with cotton or wool . . . . . . (Deer mouse)
AAA. In trees or about buildings
  B. Of bark and fibers; no lining; usually some leaves or sticks; often on an old crow's nest . . . . (Squirrel)
  BB. Of grasses, lined with feathers . . . . House sparrow

How is this student identifying the nest?

Digging Deeper

Ninety percent of all nests found in Northeastern North America will belong to these very common birds: robins, catbird, goldfinch, sparrow, Baltimore oriole, killdeer, red-winged blackbird, bank swallow, woodpecker. What are the characteristics of their nests? Use the key to help you.

Branching Out

Have you ever heard of *bird's-nest soup?* The people of Southeast Asia consider it to be a great delicacy. Use an encyclopedia and other reference books to learn more about bird's-nest soup. How are the nests collected? Which bird builds the nest? Is the whole nest used to make the soup or only a part of it? From where does the flavour of the soup actually come? Does collecting the nests do any harm to the birds?

Dead Birds

4. Dead Birds

Birds killed by cars, slaughtered chickens from a market or farm, and birds found under hydro wires and beside tall buildings can provide us with excellent material for studying the physical features of these animals. If birds which have died an accidental death are used, great care must be taken to avoid contact with germs. Only recently killed birds in good condition should be selected. Gloves should be worn when handling dead birds. The selected birds should be put in a plastic bag and the bag sealed. If the specimens are not going to be used immediately they should be frozen until needed for a specific activity. Under *no* circumstances should a bird or any other animal be killed for the activities which follow.

Bacteria, flies, crows and beetles will make short work of this bird.

Activity 1:

How does a dead bird disappear?

Have you ever wondered what happens to all the hundreds and hundreds of birds we see, when they die? Their carcasses become part of the decay cycle. *Nature's sanitation squad* goes into action and begins to decompose or break down their body tissues until only bones and feathers are left, and even they disappear in time. This activity will help you discover who works for the clean-up-squad.

Obtain a small, recently killed bird.

Find a spot where the bird can be left on the ground and covered with chicken wire fixed to the ground, to prevent larger animals from dragging the carcass away.

What purpose does the wire serve?

Observe and record what happens to the dead bird over a period of four weeks.

Observations should be made daily for the first week and then weekly thereafter.

Bird feathers—nature's creative handiwork.

Digging Deeper

How long does it take before the first creature visits the carcass?

Which creatures visited the bird's carcass first?

What parts of the bird deteriorated most rapidly? most slowly?

How much time passed before there were no more visible signs of change?

How many different kinds of animals were noted around the carcass?

Will the entire carcass disappear?

Was there any odour? When was it the strongest? How long did the carcass actually have an odour?

What is nature's sanitation squad?

Activity 2:

How can the parts of a dead bird be displayed?

Make a wing and foot collection from a variety of recently killed birds.

Cut off one wing where it joins the body, and cut off the legs at the knee joint.

Mount the wing and feet in a lifelike position on heavy cardboard. When mounting the wing, spread it out full. A neat, clear label bearing the bird's name, date mounted and the name of the person who found it should accompany each specimen.

Digging Deeper

Are the wings short and stubby, long and narrow, or broad?

Which birds have short, stubby wings?

Which birds have long, narrow wings? What type of flight would these wings allow?

What different types of feathers can be found on the wing?

How do the wing feathers compare with the tail feathers with regard to size and firmness?

How many wing feathers does the bird have?

How are the feathers attached to the bird's body?

How does the structure of a bird's legs and feet determine some of its activities?

Does a bird's foot give you any clue to what the bird eats? How?

Does the bird have claws? Are they all the same length?

Are the toes unwebbed, semiwebbed or webbed?

Are the legs long or short? What type of covering do the legs have?

Branching Out

Using the illustrations as a guide classify your birds' feet, wings and tails.

Make a collection of feathers from different parts of each bird's body, i.e., the tail, neck, wing. Mount them on stiff paper.

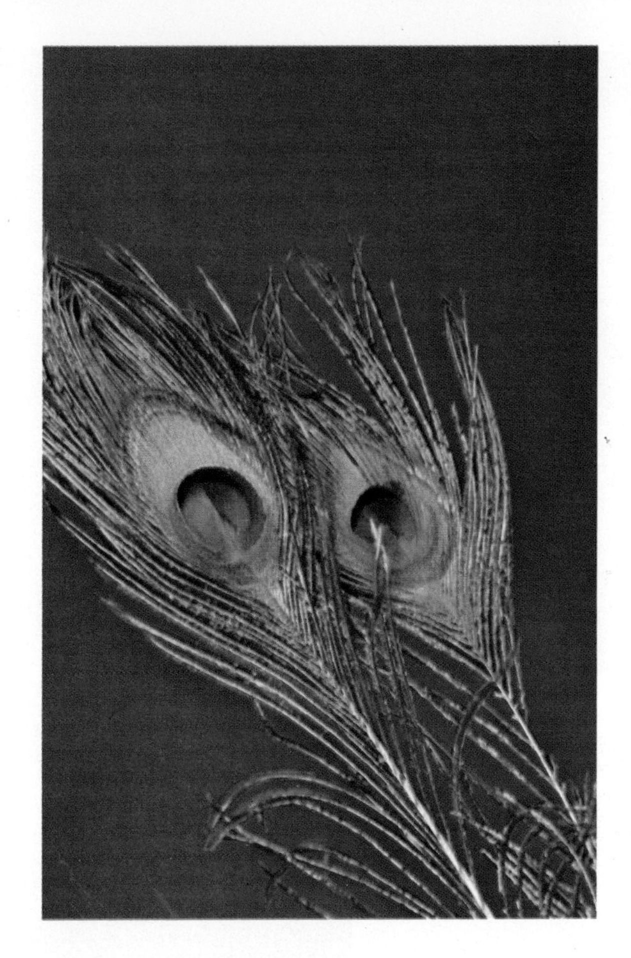

The peacock is noted for its long tail feathers marked with iridescent, eyelike spots.

Activity 3:

How can the skeleton of a bird be made?

Caution: Great care is required when doing this activity. You will be dealing with sharp instruments and boiling water so be sure you and your teacher or parents are thoroughly acquainted with the steps involved.

A good place to obtain a whole chicken is a farm, small butcher shop, or market place. Try to secure a chicken which has been plucked and gutted but still retains its head and feet. A large, old bird is preferable to a younger one since the bones of a younger bird will not be completely formed.

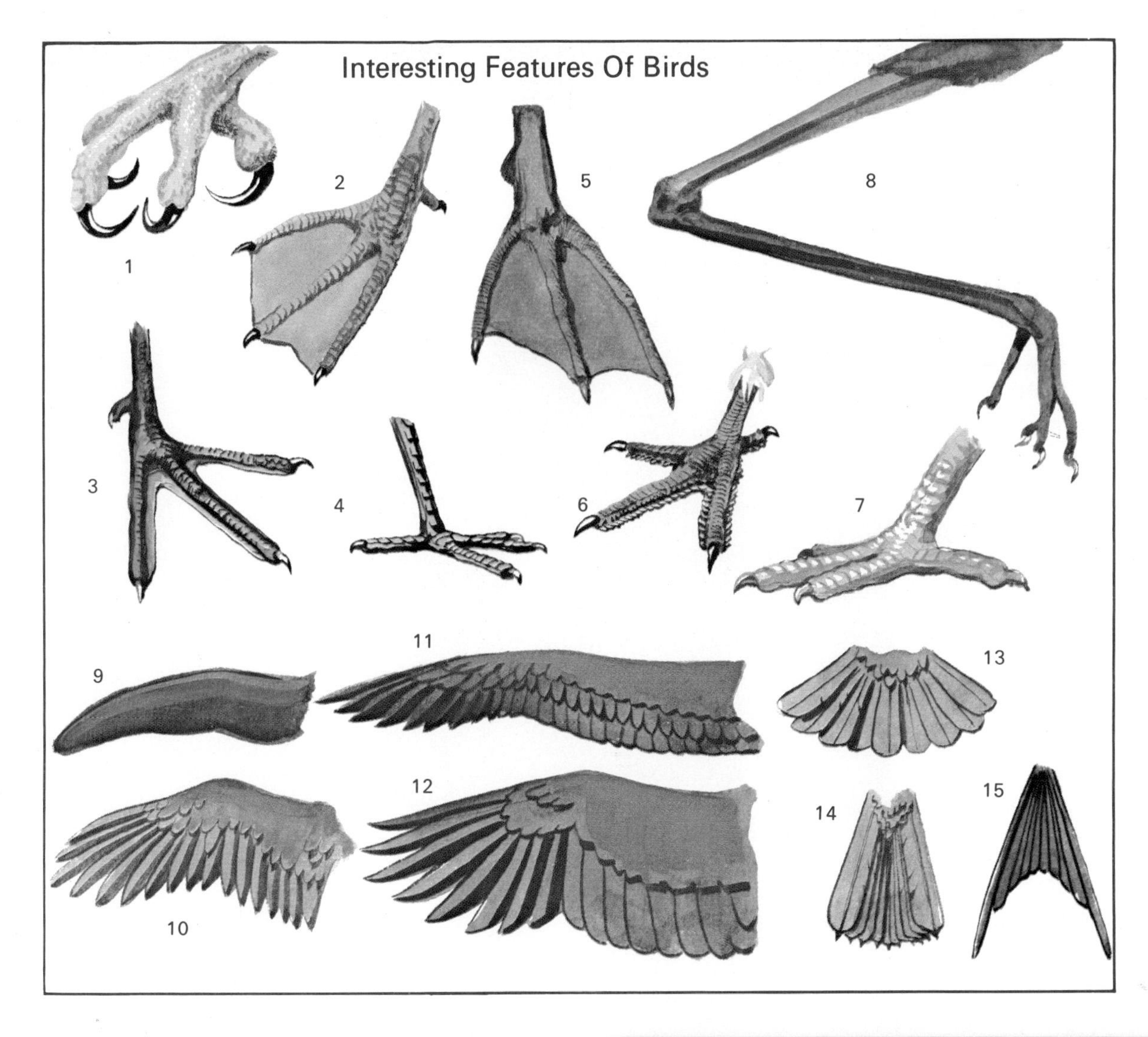

1. Curved claws of birds of prey.
2. Webbed foot of a duck.
3. Semiwebbed foot of a shore bird.
4. Straight-toed feet are not designed to grasp prey.
5. Lopsided webbed foot of a loon.
6. Bristled toe of grouse for walking on snow.
7. Chicken's toes are used for scratching.
8. Long legs of a heron help it to wade.
9. Flipperlike wings of the flightless penguin.
10. Stubby wings which allow short rapid flight.
11. Long, narrow wings which allow graceful flight.
12. Large broad wings enable a bird to sail.
13. Fanlike tail aids gliding.
14. Spine-tipped tail aids the bird when perching.
15. Forked tail of a swallow.

Obtain a chicken which still has its head and feet.

To remove the meat and soft tissue from the bones of the chicken, you will have to boil it in a large pot for 1½ to 2½ hours. Try to obtain a pot large enough to hold the entire bird or if this is not possible cut the bird up into pieces, i.e., wings, neck, feet.

Before you begin to cook your bird, feel the chicken to get an idea of where the various bones are located. Feel the head, neck, body, wings, legs, and feet.

Care must be taken when boiling your chicken. If it is cooked too long the bones will become weak and fall apart. If you don't cook it long enough the meat will be very hard to remove. The skull is the weakest part of the bone structure. It should be removed from the chicken and taken out of the water after 1 hour.

After the chicken is cooked, let it cool and then begin to remove the meat from the bones. There are two ways you can tackle this problem. Firstly, you can attempt to clean the meat from the chicken without tearing the bones apart. Secondly, you could pull the legs, wings and neck off the body of the bird and continue cleaning the meat from the bones. Bones which still have meat on them should be placed back in the pot and cooked a little longer.

Jack-knives, toothbrushes, paper clips made into probes, and running water can be employed to help get the bones clean.

Once all the bones have been cleaned, lay them out on a paper towel to dry.

Don't overcook the chicken.

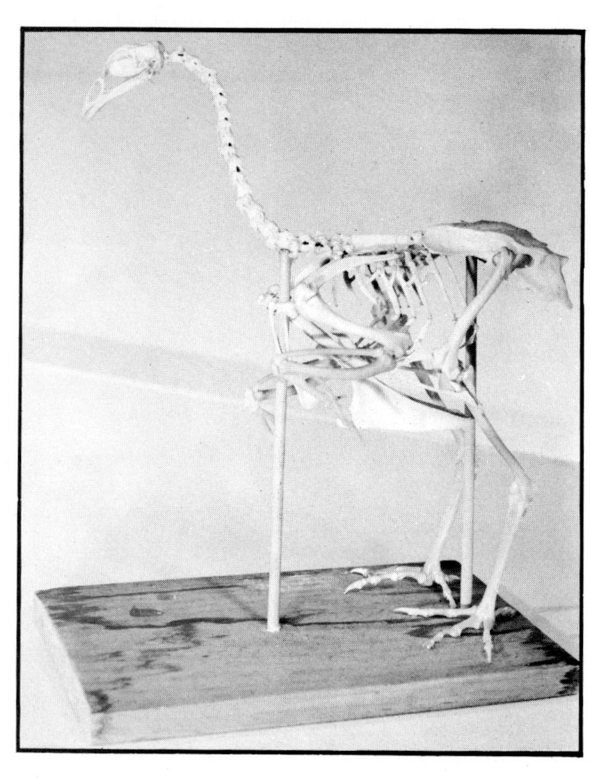

A standing skeleton of a chicken.

Before assembling bones lay them out correctly first.

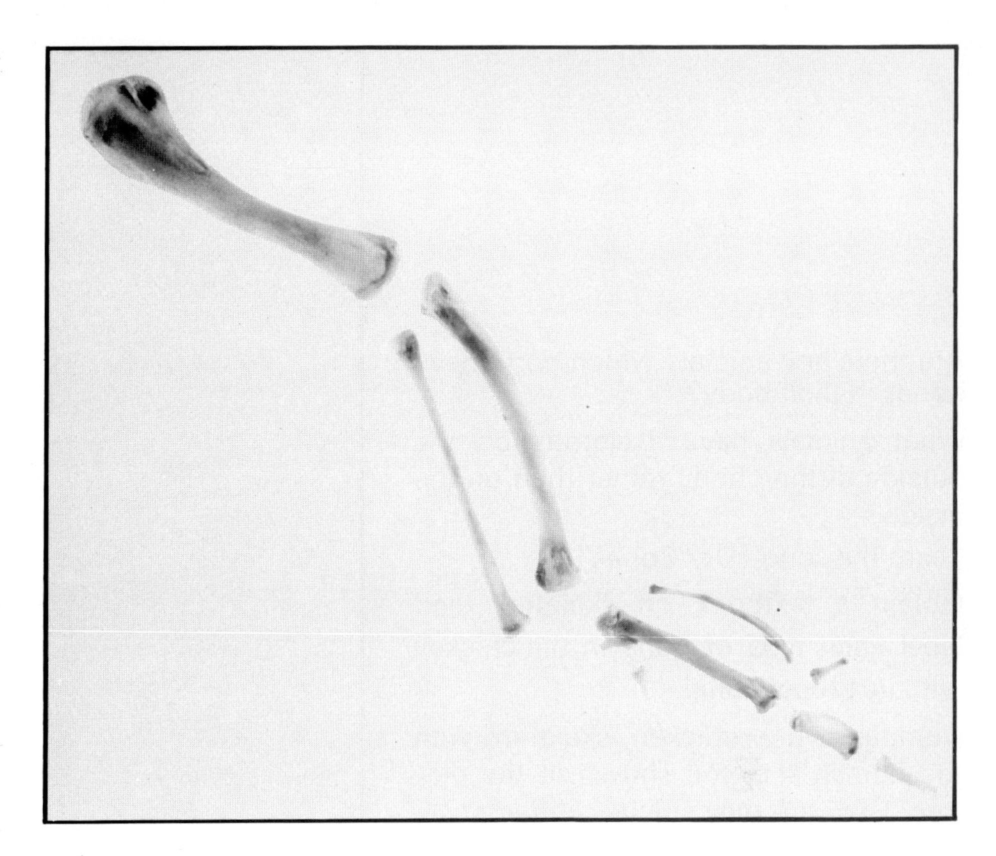

Taking the bird apart is easy, the hard part is reassembling all of the bones. This can be done by laying all the bones out flat on a stiff piece of cardboard and gluing the pieces down in their proper order. However, the alternative and the best method, but, by far the most difficult, is to make a standing skeleton. You will have to make a support for your skeleton and then glue the bones together with a quick drying glue such as airplane glue. It might be easier to assemble the feet, legs, wings, neck and head first and later attach these to the body.

Digging Deeper

How many individual bones does the chicken have in its body? How could you check your answer?

Would a young chicken have the same number of bones?

A joint is the point where two bones are joined by ligaments enabling movement. How many joints does the chicken have?

Which bone has the largest surface area?

Are all the bones the same colour?

What function do bones serve in the body?

Bones after they have been glued together.

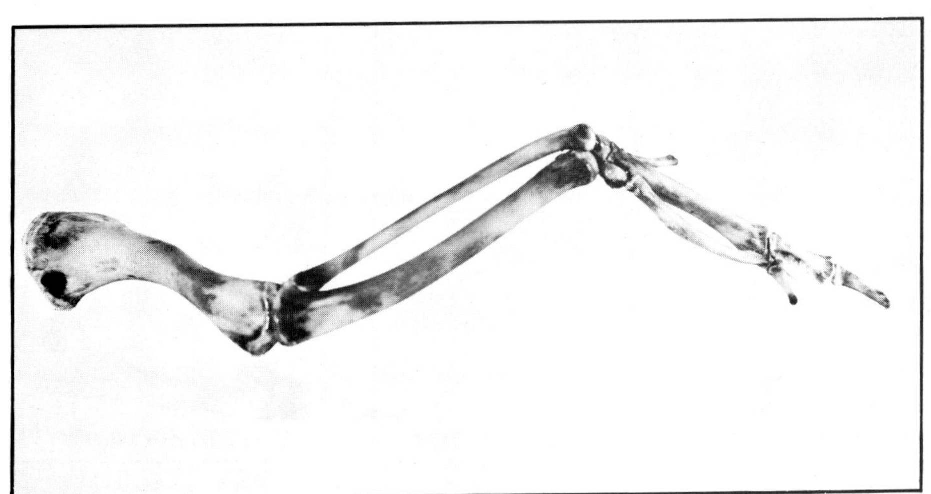

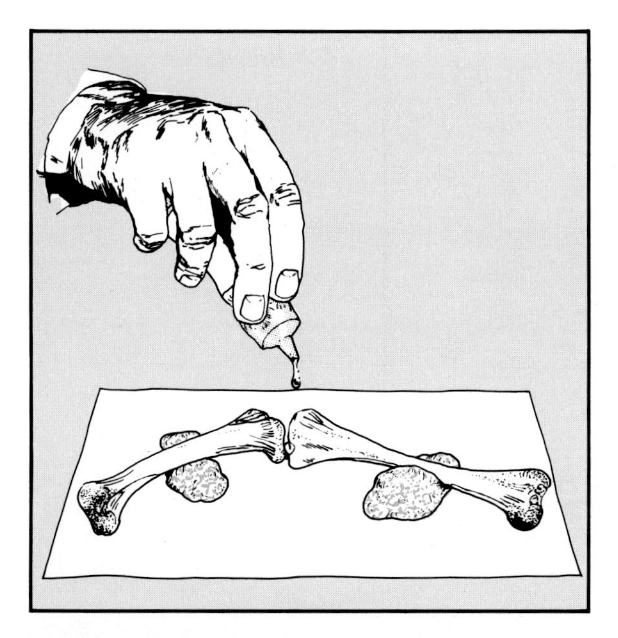

Putty or clay can be used as a holder.

Branching Out

Are there any animals which don't have bones in their body?

What animals have skeletons on the outside of their body rather than on the inside?

Learn the song "Dry Bones".

Obtain a textbook on skeletons and label each type of bone in the chicken with its proper name.

Compare your chicken skeleton with the human skeleton shown in the picture. How are they similar? different?

How do the chicken's wing bones compare with the sketch of the human arm and hand?

How many bones make up the skeleton of an adult? an infant?

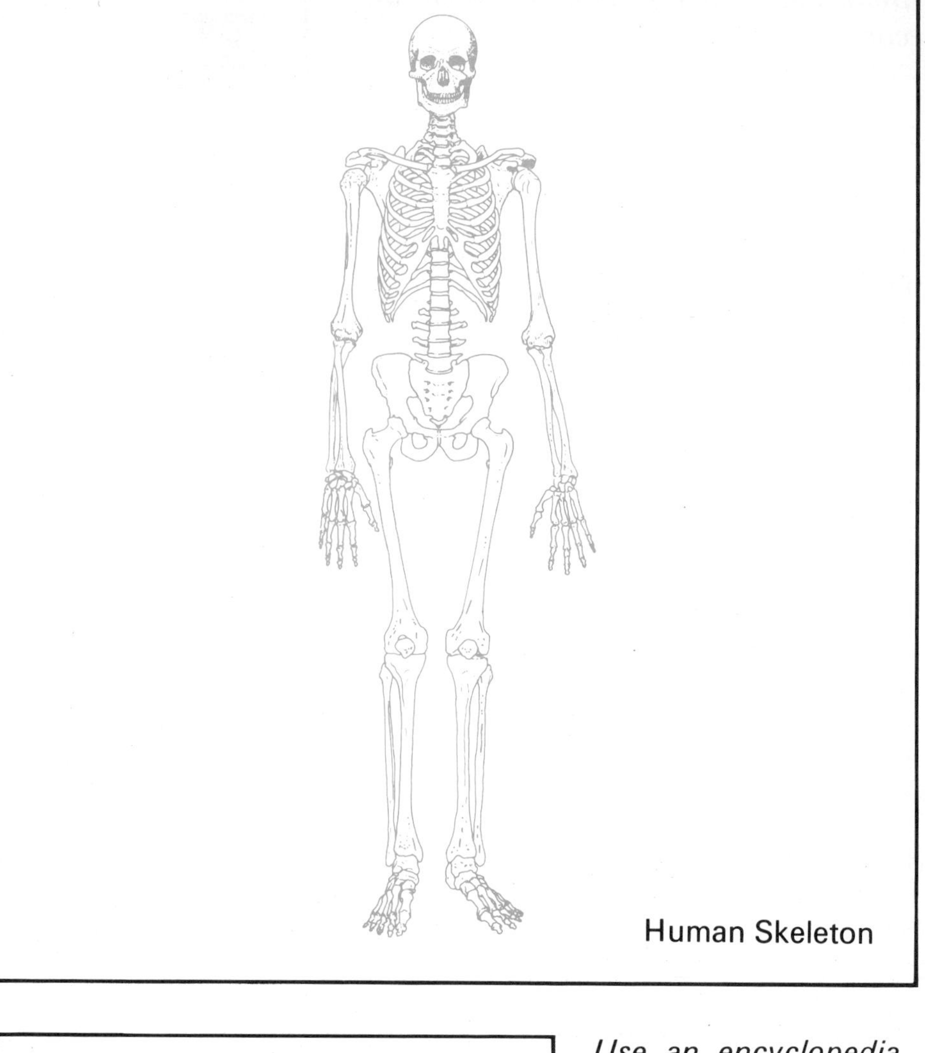

Human Skeleton

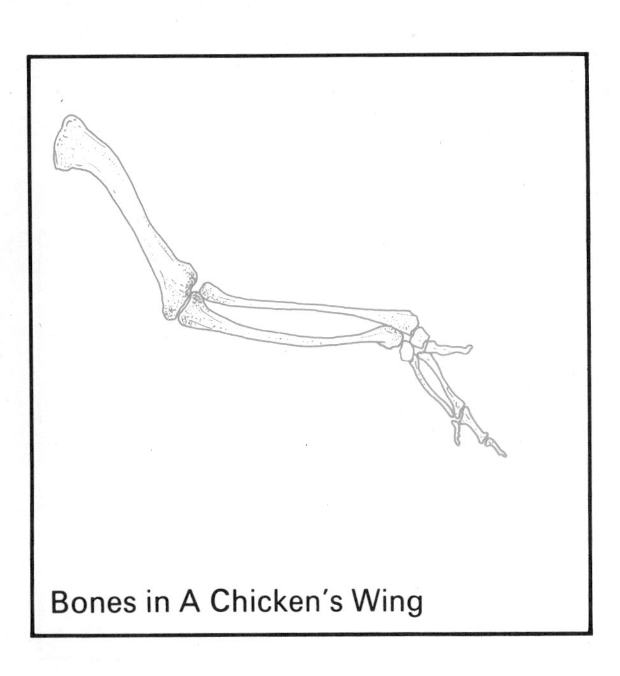

Bones in A Chicken's Wing

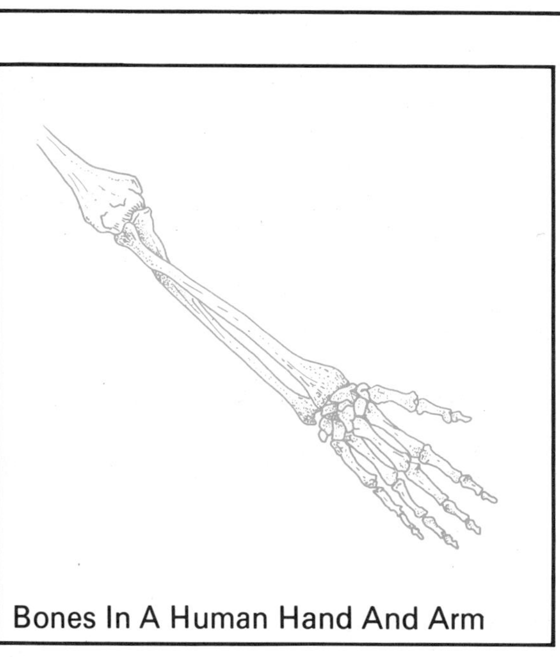

Bones In A Human Hand And Arm

Use an encyclopedia to label each of these bones with their correct name.

Make a skeleton of a fish. How many bones does a fish have? Compare it with the chicken and human skeletons. What is the biggest bone in each of these animals? the smallest bone? How do the three types of backbones differ? How do the skulls differ?

The bone data of the human and the chicken could be recorded in a table like the one shown.

Comparison of Types of Bones Found in Animals

Scientific Name of Bones	Human	Chicken
Skull	✓	
Mandible	✓	
Clavicle	✓	
Scapula	✓	
Sternum	✓	
Ribs	✓	
Humerus	✓	
Vertebral Column	✓	
Radius and Ulna	✓	
Carpals	✓	
Metacarpals	✓	
Phalanges	✓	
Pelvis	✓	
Femur	✓	
Patella	✓	
Tibia	✓	
Fibula	✓	
Tarsals	✓	
Metatarsals	✓	
Phalanges	✓	

The authors and publisher wish to thank Elementary Science Study, Education Development Center, Inc. for their assistance in writing this activity.

Activity 4:

How is a feather constructed?

Obtain a large pinion feather (wing feather) of a bird.

Examine the different parts of the feather.

Make a sketch of the entire feather and its different parts as you see them.

Examine the feathery part with a hand lens. Sketch what you see.

If possible, examine the feathery part under a microscope. Again sketch what you see.

A good way to record this type of information is by a circular diagram with labels.

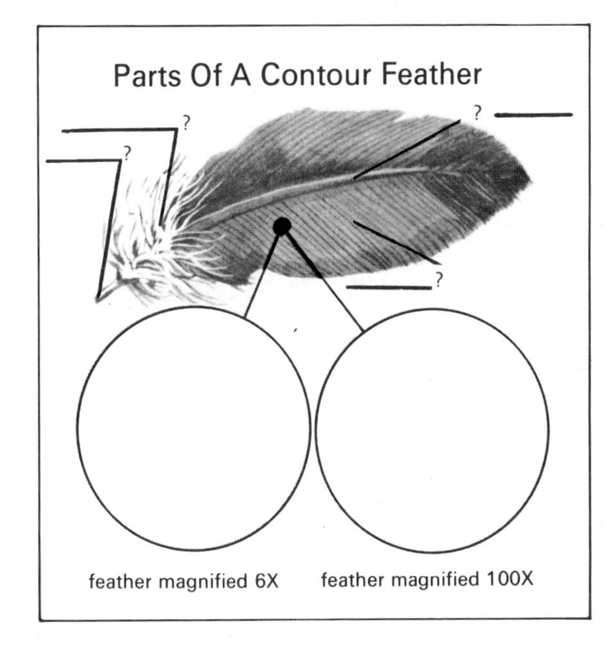

Name and sketch the parts of a contour feather.

Digging Deeper

What are all the feathers on a bird called?

What part of the feathery portion holds it together?

What fills the spaces between the parts of the feather? How would this benefit the bird?

What does the word preening mean?

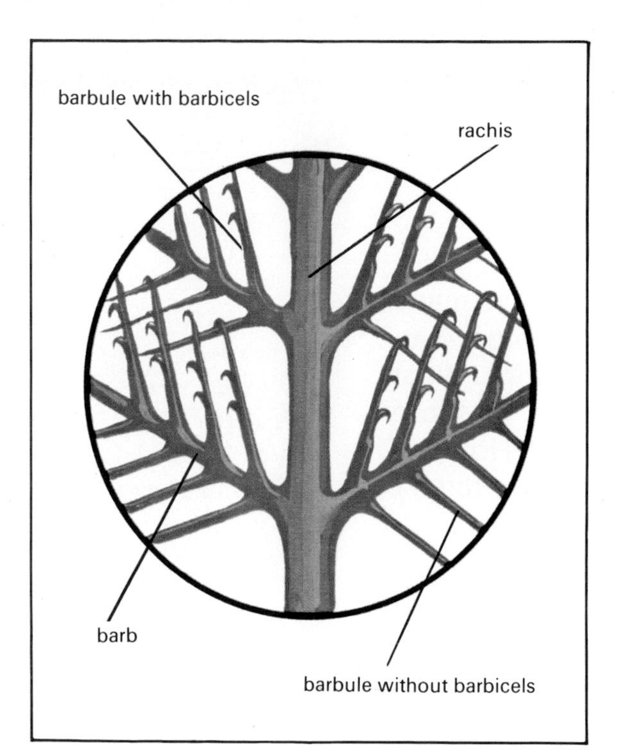

The construction of a contour feather as seen under a micro-scope.

Branching Out

Obtain a book on birds which correctly names all the parts of a bird's feather (both bulk and micro-properties) and compare your feather data with the information found in the book. Label your diagrams correctly.

Examine a variety of feathers to determine whether or not they all have the same structure.

Activity 5:

What types of feathers are found on a bird?

Make a collection of birds' feathers. The feathers could be collected from both live and dead birds. Collect feathers from different parts of a bird's body, i.e., tail, wing, breast.

Mount the feathers on a stiff piece of cardboard, grouping together the feathers that look alike.

Digging Deeper

How many different types of feathers did you find?

Scientists claim that birds have only two basic kinds of feathers. What are they?

Do the feathers from different birds have the same texture (feel)? Be sure to examine a barn owl's feathers.

What measurements could you perform on the different kinds of feathers?

How many feathers would a bird have on its body?

What are the principle flight feathers of the wing called?

Are birds born with both types of feathers on their body?

What uses does man make of feathers?

What type of feather does he use most?

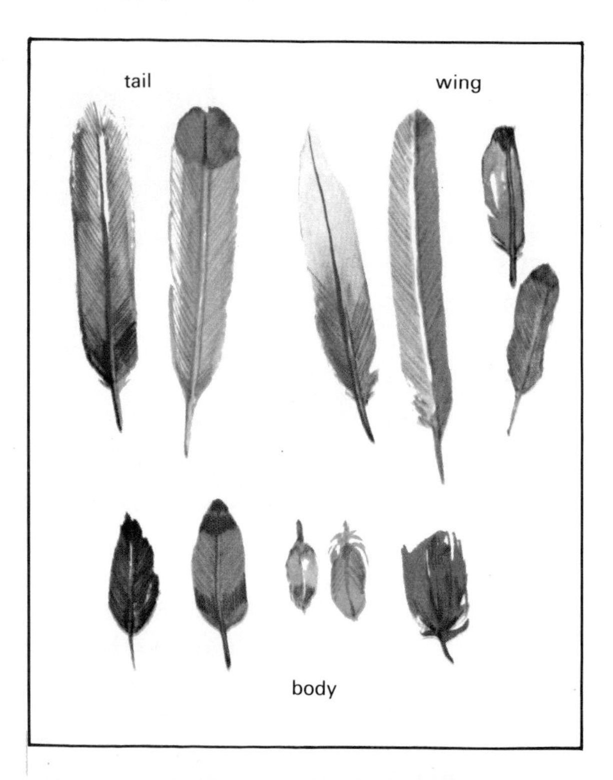

Different types of feathers.

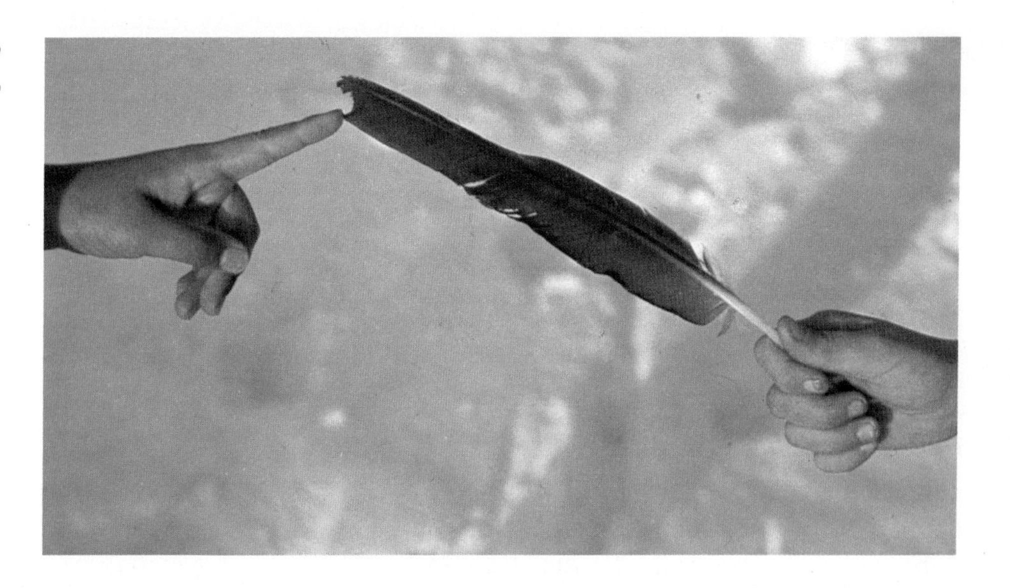

A Canada goose shed this feather. Can you detect from this picture why the Canada goose sheds its feathers?

Birds shed their feathers at least once, and sometimes several times, a year. What is this shedding process correctly called?

When looked at from different angles, some feathers appear to change colour. What are feathers like these called?

Branching Out

Water birds oil their feathers regularly to give them waterproofing and buoyancy. Obtain two domestic geese. Place both of them into a tub of water and watch them swim. Remove one of the birds from the tub and wash its feathers with a liquid dish soap mixed with lukewarm water. Put the bird back into the tub of water. What happens to the bird? Why?

Penguins are said to be birds. Do they have feathers or fur covering their bodies?

Visit your local science museum. They will have a large collection of *bird skins*. These are stuffed birds which have been laid out flat in trays for ease of studying and handling. Each bird is labelled with an identification tag. Besides the bird skins, the nests and eggs of the birds of your region will also be available for examination. Arrangements should be made with the museum beforehand regarding the time, number in the group, and exactly what it is the group wishes to see.

Emperor penguins hatch their eggs and raise their young on the bare Antarctic ice fields during the winter.

Activity 6:

How much do the bones and feathers of birds weigh?

Have you ever heard the expression, as light as a feather? Birds are tremendously light for their size. Tiny birds, such as finches and wrens, weigh less than a new pencil. Large birds, such as owls, seldom exceed 6 pounds. What makes birds so light? Try the following activity and see if you can discover some of the structural features which make birds feather weights!

A very sensitive balance will be needed for this activity. One can be readily constructed from the following materials: block of wood 2 inches by 4 inches by 8 inches, ruler with millimetre marks, 1 piece of wood 18 inches by 4 inches by 1 inch, 1 piece of wood 1 inch by 2 inches by 5 inches, some string, a piece of cardboard 3 inches by 3 inches, some glue, a darning needle, and a hacksaw blade. (If a commercial balance is available, use it to find the actual weight of the parts.)

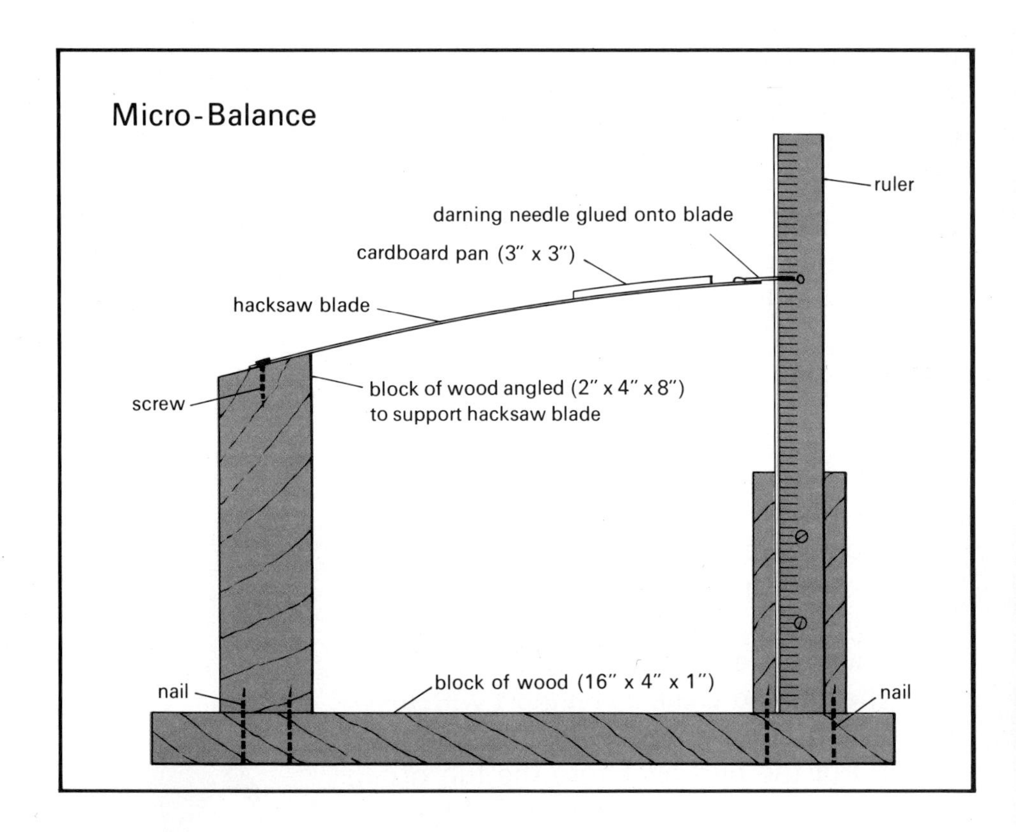

How could you calibrate your scale in grams? (1 ounce = 28 grams approximately; a new nickel weighs 5 grams, a new dime 2½ grams.) Weigh the different feathers and bones of chickens, turkeys, and other birds that you have collected.

How might this weight data best be recorded?

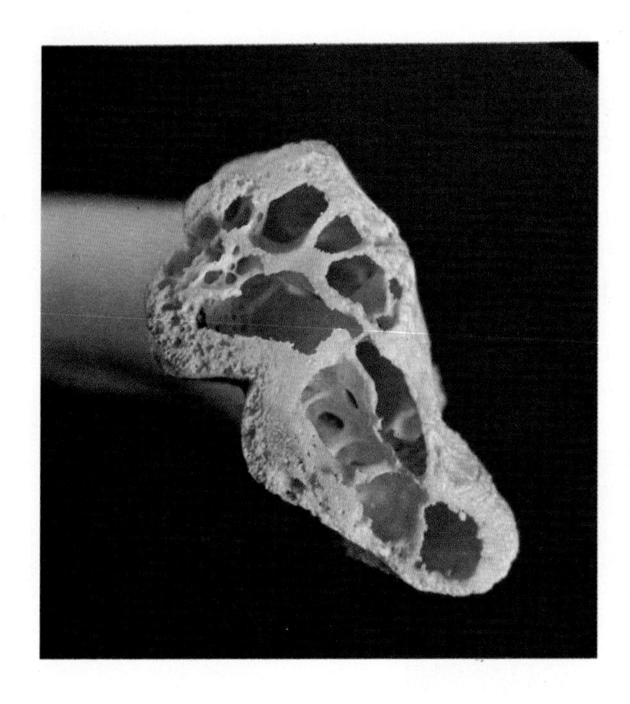

How are lightness and rigidity combined in the bones of birds?

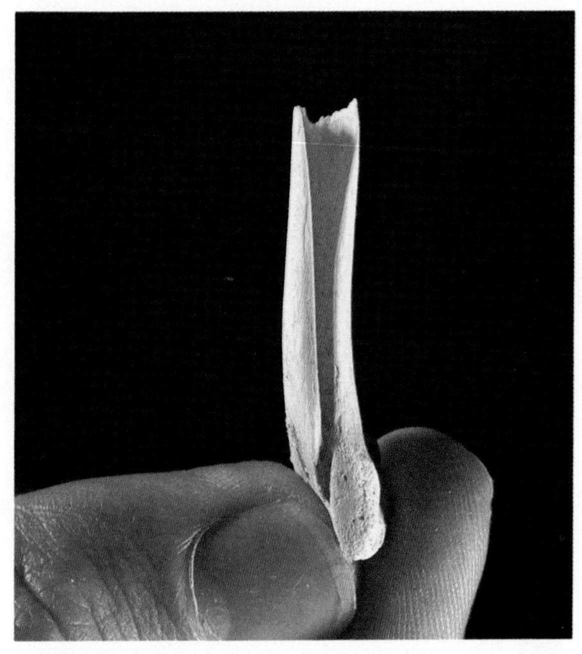

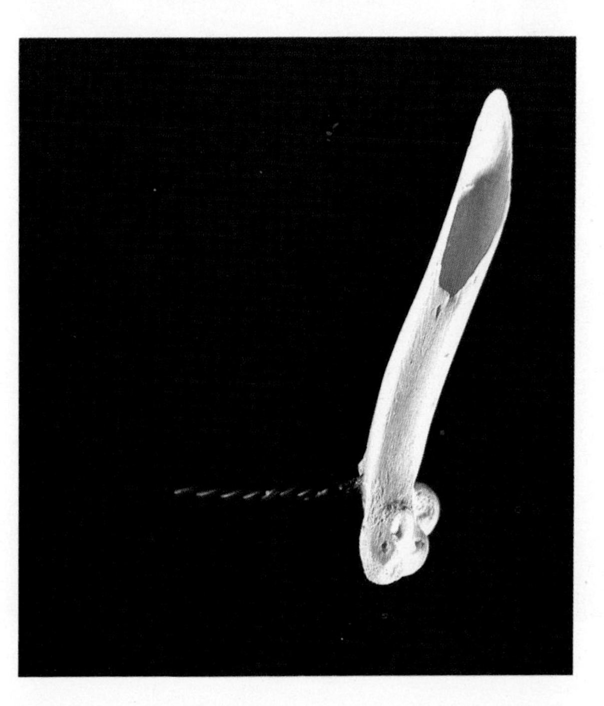

Digging Deeper

Is the expression *light as a feather* valid?

Which bone was the heaviest? How heavy is it compared to the largest feathers you weighed?

What do all the bones of a chicken weigh?

What would all the feathers of a chicken weigh?

What is inside a bird's bone?

What makes the bones so light?

What makes the feathers so light?

What is inside the quill of a feather?

Are a bird's bones strong or delicate compared to a dog's or cat's bones?

Birds have *air sacs* inside their body. What functions do they serve?

If birds are generally so light, why can we buy 24 pound turkeys?

Branching Out

Which weighs more, a pound of feathers or a pound of gold?

Visit a chicken or turkey farm. How are the birds fed? What are they fed? How many would be on a farm? What happens to the birds? To whom are they sold? What age are they when they are sold? Do wild turkeys ever weigh as much as 24 pounds?

Discover which is the largest bird in your area, the smallest. How much does each bird weigh? What is the weight of the largest bird in the world? the smallest? Compare these weights with the weights of prehistoric birds.

Fossil of Archaeopteryx, a lizardlike bird which lived about 130 million years ago.

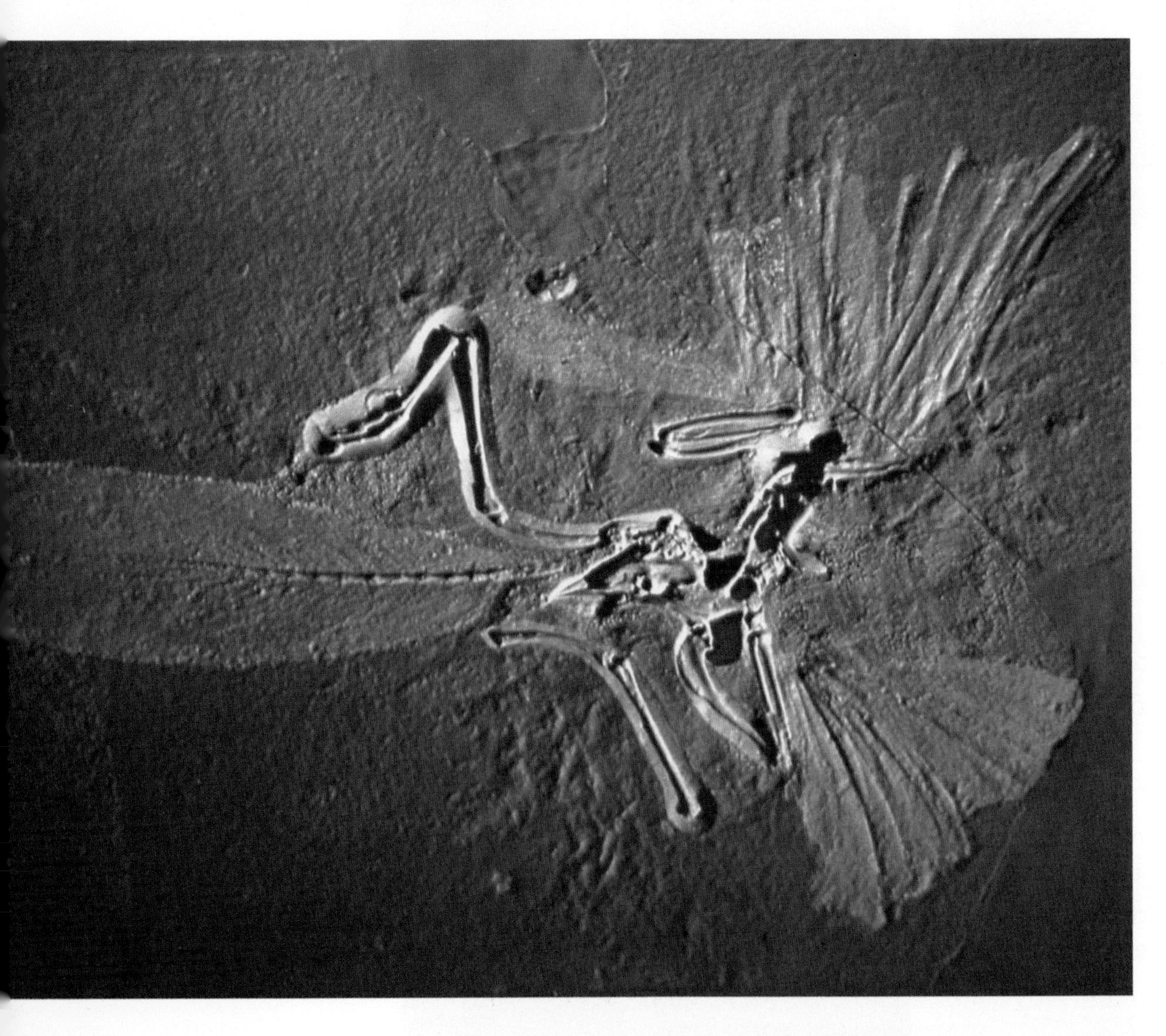

Bibliography

1. Allen, Arthur A. *The Book of Bird Life.* New York: Van Nostrand, 1930.
2. Allen, G., and Joan Denslow. *Birds.* London: Oxford University Press, 1968.
3. Armstrong, T., and Knoll, Paul W. *A Theory For The Birds.* Pasadena: Ambassador College Press, 1967.
4. Barton, Roger. *How To Watch Birds.* New York: McGraw-Hill, 1955.
5. Beecher, W. J. *Nesting Birds and the Vegetation Substrata.* Chicago: Chicago Ornithological Society, 1942.
6. Canadian Wildlife Service. *Nest Boxes for Birds.* Ottawa: Queen's Printer, 1965.
7. *Elementary School Science Project: A Comparative Study of the Development of Human and Chick Embryos.* Berkeley: University of California Press.
8. *Elementary Science Study: How To Make A Chicken Skeleton.* Toronto: McGraw-Hill, 1965.
9. Fischer, R. B. *Birds.* Ithaca, New York: New York State College of Agriculture, 1959.
10. Gentry, T. G. *Nests and Eggs of Birds of the United States.* Philadelphia: J. A. Wagenseller, 1882.
11. Gordon, E. L., and Sherwood, Mary P. *Inviting Bird Neighbours.* Ithaca, New York: New York State College of Agriculture, 1964.
12. Hann, H. W. *The Biology of Birds.* Ann Arbor, Michigan: Edward Brothers Inc., 1953.
13. Headstorm, Richard. *Birds' Nests: A Field Guide.* New York: Ives Washburn Inc., 1949.
14. Herrick, F. H. *The Home Life of Wild Birds.* New York: G. P. Putnam's Sons, 1902.
15. Herrick, F. H. *Wild Birds At Home.* New York: D. Appleton Century Co. Inc., 1935.
16. McElroy, Thos. P., Jr. *Handbook of Attracting Birds.* New York: Knopf, 1950.
17. Peterson, Roger Troy. *A Field Guide to the Birds.* New York: Houghton Mifflin, 1947.
18. Peterson, R. T. *The Birds.* New York: Time-Life Inc., 1967.
19. Reed, C. A. *North American Birds' Eggs.* New York: Doubleday, Page & Co., 1904.
20. Saunders, Aretas A. *The Lives of Wild Birds.* Garden City: Doubleday, 1954.
21. Simon, H. *The Study of Birds Made Simple.* Garden City: Doubleday & Co. Inc., 1962.
22. Wallace, George J. *An Introduction to Ornithology.* New York: The Macmillan Co., 1955.
23. Wetly, J. C. *The Life of Birds.* New York: Knopf, 1963.
24. Wolfson, A., ed. *Recent Studies in Avian Biology.* Urbana: University of Illinois Press, 1955.
25. Zim, Herbert S., and Gabrielson, Ira N. *Birds: Golden Nature Guide.* New York: Simon & Schuster, 1949.

Glossary

Altricial birds: Birds which are born helpless and almost naked, and must be fed after hatching.

$CaCO_3$: Calcium carbonate, a chemical compound widely used in making lime and portland cement.

Clutch: A nest of eggs, or the number of eggs in a nest after incubation has started.

Compass rose: A pattern found on the floor of the housing of a compass symbolizing N, S, E, and W.

Elliptical: Shaped like an oval but having both ends equal in size.

Nidology: The science of birds' nests.

Oology: The science of birds' eggs.

Orient: To place in the right relation to the points of the compass.

Palmate: Having toes united by a web, as in most swimming birds.

Pensile: Hanging, suspended, like a pendulum.

Precocial birds: Birds which are born covered with down and which can feed themselves immediately after hatching.

Preening: Trimming, dressing or smoothing feathers with the beak.

Pyriform: Pear-shaped.

Semipalmate: Having the toes joined only part way down with a web.

Semipensile: Partially supported.

Spherical: Rounded with all points on the surface the same distance from the centre.

Index of Activities

Picture Credits

Ralph Campbell
J. Kenneth Couchman
John C. MacBean
Adam Stecher
Daniel F. Wentworth
Cover, Ambassador College Photo, Miller Services.
Miller Services, *1*.
Copyright 1965 National Film Board of Canada, *2*.
Robert C. Hermes from National Audubon Society, *4*.
Ambassador College Photo, *8*.
Copyright 1968 National Film Board of Canada, *13*.
Buffalo Museum of Science, Ornithological Society, *19*.
Miller Services, *21*.
Courtesy of the New York State Conservationist, *23*.
Buffalo Museum of Science, *24*.
Courtesy of the New York State Conservationist, *29*.
Canada Wide Feature Services Ltd., *32*.
Courtesy of Photographic Division, Ontario Dept. of Agriculture and Foods, Ontario Agricultural College, University of Guelph, *38*.
Photos by Richard D. Robinson, *41* & *43*.
From *Nest Boxes* by William H. Carrick, Queen's Printer, 1965, *50* & *51*.
From *The Book of Bird Life* by A. A. Allen. Copyright 1930, 1961 by Litton Educational Publishing, Inc., by permission of D. Van Nostrand Co., *53-57*.
Ambassador College Photos, *59* & *61*.
From *How to Make a Chicken Skeleton* by Elementary Science Study, Webster Division, McGraw-Hill Book Co. Copyright 1965 by Education Development Center, Inc., *64* & *65*.
Photo by Warren Hamilton, *69*.
Ambassador College Photos, *71*.
Courtesy of The American Museum of Natural History, *72*.